CONFERENCE
PROCEEDINGS

TIMBER
AND THE BUILT
ENVIRONMENT
CONFERENCE

Edited by
Janet Kleboe

Published by
Historic Scotland

ISBN 1 904966 00 4
© Crown Copyright
Edinburgh 2004

Commissioned by
TECHNICAL
CONSERVATION,
RESEARCH AND
EDUCATION
GROUP

SCOTTISH EXECUTIVE

Forestry Commission

wood. for

Publisher's Note:

The views expressed in the conference papers are the contributors' and not necessarily those of Historic Scotland.

CONTENTS

PROGRAMME

TIMBER AND THE BUILT ENVIRONMENT: Day 1

THURSDAY 17 OCTOBER 2002

08.30 – 09.30   Registration and Coffee

09.30 – 09.45   Welcome and Introduction: **Graeme Munro**, Director & Chief Executive, Historic Scotland

09.45 – 09.50   Chair: **Ingval Maxwell**, Director, TCRE, Historic Scotland

Session A
SUSTAINABLE TIMBER: AN INTRODUCTION

09.50 – 10.25   Sustainable timber production and sourcing – **David Bills**, Director General, Forestry Commission

10.25 – 11.00   Timber as part of the sustainable future – **Howard Liddell**, GAIA Architects

11.00 – 11.30   COFFEE

Session B
TRADITIONS AND HISTORY OF TIMBER CONSTRUCTION

11.30 – 12.00   Vernacular use of timber – **Chris McGregor**, Historic Scotland

12.00 – 12.30   Timber in Scottish historic buildings – **Geoffrey Stell**, Royal Commission on the Ancient and Historic Monuments of Scotland

12.30 – 13.00   Timber engineering in a heritage context – **Robert Bowles**, Alan Baxter & Associates

13.00 – 14.15   LUNCH (under individual arrangements)

Session C
SUSTAINING TIMBER IN THE HERITAGE ENVIRONMENT

14.15 – 14.40   Designing out timber deterioration: environmentally sustainable conservation solutions – **Jagjit Singh**, Environmental Building Solutions Ltd

14.40 – 15.05   Good management: avoiding dry rot decay – **John Palfreyman**, University of Abertay, Dundee

15.05 – 15.30   Preventing insect attack – **Brian Ridout**, Ridout Associates

15.30 – 16.00   TEA

Session D
SCOTTISH CASE STUDIES

16.00 – 16.15   Stirling Castle, Great Hall hammer beam roof – **Peter Buchanan**, Historic Scotland

16.15 – 16.30   Scottish Seabird Centre, North Berwick – **Sue Whittle**, Simpson & Brown Architects

16.30 – 16.45   The Hub – **Ben Tindall**, Benjamin Tindall Architects

16.45 – 17.00   Housing in the Highlands – **Neil Stephen**, Dualchas Architects

17.00 – 17.15   Glencoe Visitor Centre – **Chris Morgan**, GAIA Architects

17.15 – 17.30   Close: **Ingval Maxwell**

TIMBER AND THE BUILT ENVIRONMENT: Day 2

FRIDAY 18 OCTOBER 2002

08.30 – 9.00   Registration and Coffee

Session E
IMPACTS ON THE NEW-BUILD ENVIRONMENT: LEARNING FROM THE PAST

09.00 – 09.10   Chair: **Bob McIntosh**, Chief Executive, Forest Enterprise

09.10 – 09.40   Wood as a design material – **Ivor Davies**

09.40 – 10.20   Tradition and present: wood in Finnish architecture – **Hannu Tikka**, Artto Palo Rossi Tikka Architects

10.20 – 11.00   Norwegian experience – **Ole Wiig**, Narud-Stokke-Wiig Architects

11.00 – 11.30   COFFEE

Session F
ACHIEVING A HEALTHY FUTURE

11.30 – 12.00   Healthy designs and healthy buildings – **John Gilbert**, John Gilbert Architects

12.00 – 12.30   The possible impacts of climate change: design and conservation – **Stephen Garvin**, Director, BRE Scotland

12.30 – 13.00   Environmental aspects of timber in construction – **Peter Bonfield**, Director, Centre for Timber Technology and Construction, BRE

13.00 – 14.15   LUNCH (under individual arrangements)

Session G
INNOVATIVE USE OF TIMBER

14.15 – 14.40   Timber frames in a heritage context – **Richard Harris**, Director, Weald and Downland Museum

14.40 – 15.10   Modern timber frame – **Stewart Dalgarno**, Stewart Milne Timber Systems

15.10 – 15.30   Oslo Airport terminal – **Ole Wiig**, Narud-Stokke-Wiig Architects

15.30 – 15.50   Sibelius Hall, Finland – **Hannu Tikka**, Artto Palo Rossi Tikka Architects

15.50 – 16.10   Maggie's Centre – **James Stephen**, James F Stephen Architects

16.10 – 16.40   TEA

Session H

16.40 – 17.40   DISCUSSION PANEL

Chair: **Sebastian Tombs**, Chief Executive, Royal Incorporation of Architects in Scotland

17.40 – 18.00   CONCLUSIONS AND SUMMING UP: **Ingval Maxwell**

FOREWORD

Timber is a material with great potential. It is one of the world's oldest constructional and decorative design materials, and is widely used today. It is also, by its very nature, a growing resource that impacts positively on our climate and environment.

The aim of the Timber and the Built Environment Conference held in Edinburgh on 17-18th October 2002 was to broaden an understanding of the potential of timber as a building material. It also intended to offer inspiration and awareness to designers, and others, to assist them in stimulating a future demand for indigenously produced timber buildings in Scotland. The underlying theme was to encourage and facilitate developing markets for the use of timber from Scottish broadleaved woodlands.

The Conference ably provided a venue for the dissemination of relevant up to date knowledge and information to a wide audience. It focussed on the production, design and specification of timber; created a heightened awareness of its context and use; examined the relationship between decay organisms, the material itself, and environmental conditions surrounding its specification and application. Particular emphasis was placed on understanding the benefits of environmental monitoring and control; deterioration mechanisms; informing on multi-disciplinary solutions, on maintenance and bio-deterioration.

The programme intention aimed to promote and develop a better understanding of timber by bringing together experts in the conservation and construction of a range of different building types. In presenting a series of national and international case studies, speakers covered a variety of topics in the tradition, and history, of building with timber, and offered a captivating insight into current, innovative, uses. Aimed at practitioners in the building and timber industries, that programme is distilled in the following Proceedings. In offering the full presentations, it is hoped that this volume will help engender future confidence in the adoption of sustainably produced timber products in a way that also supports the intentions of the Scottish Executive's Policy on Architecture.

In publishing this volume, particular thanks are due to all contributors, and to the Scottish Executive's Architecture Policy Unit, the Forestry Commission, Wood for Good, Environmental Building Solutions, the Royal Incorporation of Architects in Scotland, and Abertay University, amongst many others, who assisted in making the Conference so successful.

Ingval Maxwell OBE
Director
Technical Conservation, Research
and Education Group,
Historic Scotland,
Edinburgh

March 2004

SUSTAINABLE TIMBER

David Bills, Director General, Forestry Commission

Despite all the wonderful things you hear about timber, there is always a caveat, and that caveat is that it should come from well-managed forests. And I am sure that we will get many papers on the technical, economic and social issues. We all have our own timber stories to tell and recently while I was away in South Africa, my cupola collapsed. Now this is a wooden cupola, 4 storeys up in a Victorian town house, and it created a huge amount of damage when it collapsed. As the Director-General of the Forestry Commission I have to say I was severely tempted to have an aluminium cupola replacement. Then I thought about it and I diagnosed the problem, and indeed there had been some rot set in to the collar beam. The actual structure in the rafters had lasted quite well but it was the anchorage point and one of the legs that failed. The whole twisting moment had caused the structure to shatter and fall 3 storeys to street level causing. The timber cupola had been there since 1867, and that's not too bad. And furthermore, during that period the actual glazing bars, and the visible bits weren't rotten. They had stood the test of time. And the qualification is always, that the timber must be correctly installed, and if we can keep the water away, it will last. But I am not here to talk about installation, I am here to talk about sourcing timber. I want to issue a general warning that although timber can provide so many solutions to building, environmental and social problems, it can contribute to another problem, and that is by undermining the sustainability of the global forest resource. The fundamental questions that need to be asked are:

- Has the timber come from a forest that has been managed sustainably?

  To manage sustainably means far more than just replanting the trees that are harvested.

- Is the logging consistent with the law of the land?

  Laws can either be wilfully broken or in some countries, unfortunately, there is insufficient capacity for people to either know about the law, or to enforce the law.)

- Is the site being managed in such a way as to conserve the long-term productivity?

For example soil and water conservation.

Soil and water conservation is important to the biological sustainability of the resource, and within that ecosystem of course, there can be rare and endangered species, and breeding populations, migratory populations – all this can be threatened. Have local communities been displaced or otherwise had their life disrupted? We are all aware of sweatshops and factories in some developing countries. The fact that the removal of the forest can impact on communities where access to that forest has been very important to their own sustenance, and perhaps to their own industry. Has the labour, which has been employed in the sawmill, or the workshop, been given dignity and appropriate support in terms of occupation, health and safety? To use timber without knowing these problems, and without knowing the answers to these questions, can create one problem whilst solving another. And the fact is we have to recognise that today, forest ecosystems are under threat.

It was in December 2001 that the Secretary-General of the United Nations Conference on Environment and Development produced a review of progress achieved in implementing the UN Conference of Environment and Development, commonly known as the Rio Earth Summit, held in Johannesburg ten years ago. It was a bleak review. It states in summary that forests are of great importance to people worldwide: socially, economically and environmentally, but that little progress has been made in tackling the high rate of deforestation in developing countries. Although in some regions – and these are my words now – notably Europe, the area of forest biomass has increased, there is overall a net loss of area and business on a global scale. Moreover, much of what is being done, and much of what is being lost involves what we call primary forest: mature natural forests, which often provide unique habitats for rare and endangered species. There are more estimates given in Johannesburg where it states that up to 35 million acres of tropical rainforest is being removed yearly. This is 1.8 times the area of Scotland or 75% of the area of the United Kingdom.

It is not just the timber trade, which is causing forest loss and degradation. There are activities associated with land clearing for cash crops, subsistence agriculture and intensive fuel wood gathering. These contribute to a greater share of the problem than does logging for timber without sustainable forest management. The timber trade is increasingly global and is very much a topic for all governments with illegal timber trade high on the agenda. Illegal timber trade robs governments of revenues, which often fund other illegal activities. It has been estimated that 15% of timber and timber products are illegal. Also, there are logging operations which, although sanctioned by the relevant authority, are clearly unsustainable and often within important and diminished forest ecosystems. Nevertheless, with a fairly rigid definition of legality, it is estimated that 15% of global trade is illegal, and even the governments affected want to see it stop. This money is being siphoned off and used for things like arms and drugs. This destabilises the social system. There has been a rise in the interest and practise of forest and timber certification. This has been particularly true of the United Kingdom which, along with the USA and Japan, make up the top 3 importing countries. However, the emergence of China, as a net importer, may well mean that before long, China will have replaced the UK and the increased demand for timber will create another huge pressure on the rainforests and illegal logging.

Certification is one way of providing a means of insurance to the consumer of the finished product that their purchasing decision is not supporting illegal and unsustainable forest practices. There are a number of certification systems operating and unfortunately there is a danger of confusion as the schemes often compete with one another for the attention of the trade. It is the Forest Stewardship Council Scheme, linked to the United Kingdom Woodland Assurance Standard which enjoys the most support in this country, and is perhaps the most universally recognised. To be effective in giving assurance of sustainable forest management, a certification system must have 3 elements: it must have a forest management standard, based on the fundamental principles of sustainable forest management, against which the forest management system being applied to a specific forest can be audited.

- In this country, as I have said, it is the United Kingdom Woodland Assurance Standard. A Sustainable Forest Management Standard goes beyond the standard, which involves the maintenance of the productivity of the forest. A Standard will require compliance with the law of the land, a respect for cultural heritage, and the rights of contemporary, indigenous people. It will require the maintenance of existing access arrangements, and that those who are employed in the forest's activities are treated fairly and with dignity.

- The second requirement is a chain of custody that can be audited to insure that products from the sustainable forest are indeed those, which the customer purchases. This means that the supply chain from the forest, to the mill, to the distributor,

to the end user, to the retailer must also be certified. It is very difficult for engineers, architects or specifiers to be sure they are receiving the full benefits of certification. We are not just certifying that the wood is produced sustainably, but that this piece of wood, in that beam, in that purchase, in that specification, that ends up in the construction, is indeed the piece of wood that has come from a certified forest.

- The third element is the existence of a credible, independent authority who accredits the assessors, and who owns a label that is trusted, well recognised and promoted.

This has been the strength of the FSC against the various industry certification schemes. Although many industry certification schemes are of great quality, they simply don't have the credibility of the FSC Scheme. This Scheme is actively supported by the World Wide Fund for Nature and it is the WWF and others that promote the Scheme, and there is nothing quite like having the independent third party with disinterested expert accreditation by a body like the WWF. In civil society today, the reality is the World Wide Fund are more likely to be trusted than government, university academics, or the heads of professional associations. However, certification is not the answer to all our problems. Timber imported into the United Kingdom from well-managed forests may not be certified. There is simply a lack of capacity in the certification industry whereby all wood from well-managed forests is certified. Furthermore, wood from some developing countries is coming from quite well managed forests. The institutions, the systems, the documentation and the chain of custody are not developed to provide a proper chain of custody and certification. The paradox is that not to use this wood, could penalise the developing country. It could persuade people to give up ad use a material other than wood. The worst situation is that if wood from well-managed forests can not be sold or isn't sold, because it is not certified, then that resource can lose value. The loss of value means loss of interest in the management and protection of timber as a resource. For countries that are relying very much on their natural resources, the long-term management of those natural resources provides the basis for their economic development. The question is, just who is it that wants the assurance that the wood they use comes from a sustainable forest? The kinds of consumer who may be buying from a do-it-yourself store or a finished product like a door, or a chair, or a wooden spoon. If for example I was in a store like Sainsbury's, and I had a choice between a 25p wooden spoon and a 90p wooden spoon with the FSC logo, I would buy the spoon with the FSC logo. At that level, it certainly does work. But does it work further back down the chain where the bigger amounts of timber are being used? There is evidence that it is beginning to. There are many distributors and retailers using their "muscle", and demonstrating preference for ecolabelling, irrespective of what the consumer wants. B&Q may argue that they want to apply a philosophy of corporate and civic responsibility to purchasing. They do so, because customers, shareholders and employees want it. In the UK, it is estimated that the 95+ buyers group is interested in certification and is committed to give strong preference to certified wood. They have stated a preference for the FSC-labelled timber. It is estimated that this group account for as much as 30% of the UK timber and forest product trade. More and more people, from local authorities, architects and engineers, are taking an interest in the provenance of the timber industry. This interest is generated from a number of sources and for a number of reasons. Professional associations demonstrating civic responsibility, government guidelines for ecofriendly purchasing, and the governments increasing interest in the requirement for government-funding purchasers to take timber certification into account will have an effect. We can also reasonably anticipate that a better-educated and increasingly wealthy community, exposed by the media to problems of climate change, forest degradation and species loss, will begin to take an increasing interest in doing their bit as consumers. Skilful advertising will promote these issues and demonstrate how people's consumption decisions can be improved. You may be aware of the 'Wood for Good' generic market promotion campaign. Our market research has said that contrary to what was perceived before we did the research, there is a significant interest being exhibited by opinion leaders and by consumers in general about the properties of wood. Wood is interesting in terms of carbon sequestration, lifecycle analysis, embedded energy issues, insulation properties, and of course the sustainable forest management issues. The Wood for Good campaign is producing advertising material that talks about the benefits of using wood, beyond the technical and architectural benefits. The UK government has also been proactive. It is committed to seeking timber products from legally and sustainably managed sources.

The Forestry Commission's achievement was to bring forward the United Kingdom Woodland Assurance Standard for certification and the certification of the entire Public Estate, that is the entire Forest Enterprise estate. This is recognised as a world first in terms of a public or a nation's public estate being certified. In recognition of this achievement the forestry Commission received the "Gift to the Earth Award" from the World Wide Fund for Nature.

The question is asked how it is that monolith block of

even aged Spruce can be certified by SFC? Well the great thing about certification is that it does not necessarily make a judgement on what you have, that's the past, that's the history. The WWF is interested in what the Forestry Commission is doing to enrich forests, to break up the age structures, to increase the bio diversity, to plant other species within, to engage the local communities and to make the forests more accessible to people.

There have been huge changes in the Forestry Commission's approach to forestry and forestry management over the last 10 – 20 years. The United Kingdom government has taken a lead internationally with its public procurement policy for wood products. It is also developing measures to combat illegal logging and the international trade in illegally logged timber and timber products. At the recent meeting of the International Forest forum in New York other major importers of wood such as Japan, and the USA, showed real interest in the United Kingdom government action. This action is in the form of guidance.

The guidance will help government Procurement Officers to make informed choices about the source of supply for timber. It won't be compulsory to get certified timber because the fact is a lot of good timber coming into Britain cannot be certified. However, it will provide some general information on how you can be reasonably assured that the timber you are getting is from well managed forests. There will also be a monitoring element where government departments will be required to report at the end of the year their timber purchasing activities. This sort of activity is supported by the British Timber Trade Federation, which has worked in partnership with the British government to promulgate a Code of Conduct for its membership. The membership is made up of the importers of timber in this country – and remember 80% of forest products in this country are imported. In addition the British Timber Trade Federation has negotiated an agreement with Indonesian exporters, and this agreement is in accord with the UK and Indonesian governments. It should go some way to controlling illegal logging.

These activities and others are being carried forward in a partnership. The UK Forestry Partnership is made up of environmental engineers, the United Kingdom Forest Growers and the processing industry, the Timber Trade Federation as I mentioned before, the UK government. The partnership was announced at the WSD conference in the summit in Johannesburg this year. The message was ostensibly this, that the UK has got its house in order with the domestic forest growing and conversion industry, and it is taking the lead to control trade in products from illegal sources of timber. Certification was promoted as important in linking the consumer to environmentally sound purchasing decisions. The United Kingdom partnership will continue and has continued and will be active well past the Johannesburg conference. It was not just an event for the Johannesburg conference. A programme of work is being pursued. So to summarise, you have heard that wood, a traditional material, can be used in modern ways as a high performance construction material. Wood is an environmentally compatible material with a positive role in carbon storage and with embedded energy. Building systems using wood are thermally efficient. Moreover, wood is generally recyclable, non-toxic and biodegradable. I don't think we know of any other building material that can compete with all these benefits. And, if it comes from forests managed sustainably then it will be a part of a sustainable system providing wood and a range of other benefits increasingly valued by the consumer. And one way of ensuring that wood is from sustainable forests is to seek wood, which has been certified under a respected certification scheme. Again, I have to confess it is tough. Not all wood from well-managed forests is or will be certified, and in the medium term there will probably be a need for purchasers and specifiers to have an intelligent or well-informed approach to their choice of timber. You are going to have to do some homework. We cannot give you all you need. But it would be a pity if the uncertainty of the provenance of origin of wood influenced specifiers to favour non-wood substitutes, which themselves can pose environmental problems. Wood might be considered by some an old-fashioned, traditional construction material. But it is a material, which I believe, has come of age. It will come of age in this next decade as it is increasingly recognised as an environmentally compatible material with a great potential to help solve many of the problems of the world. Again and always with the important caveat that it must come from well managed forests. Many of you here are a part of the wood supply chain, and I urge you to inform yourself of the environmental issues, and to do your bit to promote the use of wood from well managed forests to your colleagues and clients In this way, you are not only providing them with an innovative and cost-effective solution to their immediate construction problems, but you are doing your bit to combat climate change and to conserve the world's forests in a healthy state. In a nutshell, we promote wood; we should all promote wood for its benefits to your customers, and for its wider benefits to the environment. But that wood must come from well managed forests.

TIMBER AS PART OF THE SUSTAINABLE FUTURE

Howard Liddell, GAIA Architects

Timber is a fantastically sustainable material, and it is generally regarded by ecological designers as a fail-safe material, and in the main it is. However, it is not a ubiquitous material in the sense that it solves all problems - it does have its drawbacks.

A building is constructed within the 4 principles of earth, air, fire and water and the great thing about a tree is that, through photosynthesis, it combines all these key elements within which a building is constructed. However, timber has for far too long been seen as something temporary and short-term when in fact it is a very long-term material. What I would like to do is look at the life-cycle of timber and look at where the good, bad and indifferent aspects of timber are.

So let's take the first part of that cycle, the harvesting. To some extent there is a problem in knowing to what extent timber is 'green' - the FCS label is fine, but we prefer to try and source all our timber in Scotland if we can, so we know where the tree is coming from. There is scepticism regarding labelling, and some of the reasons for that are to do with biodiversity, ecology and the wider view. Many thousands of square kilometres of Amazonian rainforest continue to disappear every year, and this is particularly worrying for biodiversity – 90% of the worlds species are in the rainforest. The Amazon has 3000 species of trees of which only 30 are commercially viable. Logging techniques can be so destructive that they cannot support more than 2 extraction cycles. The trees are taken off by chains, dragging with them the very thin layer of humus. Deforested land is normally expected to be turned into farmland, but the lack of soil leads to poor plant cover, and so there is nothing to protect bare soil from being washed away by the rain. The result is a very unproductive landscape.

Throughout the last century the percentage of forest cover in Scotland went from 5 to at least 17%. Italy is about the European average of 37%. Interestingly, Brazil is 64%, and Sweden and Finland have similar percentages. So Scotland is some way behind the rest of Europe. I am absolutely committed to the idea that reforesting Scotland is the best thing that we could possibly do, but we must do it sensibly and in accordance with demand.

The second part of the cycle - once the trees have been harvested - is particularly interesting because, despite being very big, logs are not actually worth a great deal.

Their value only becomes significant once something is done with them. This part of the cycle is very much linked to the next part - where are you going to exploit the added value? We recently conducted a study for the European Community into the potential of round poles for adding value to local communities in the northern periphery of the EU. It is interesting to note the difference, not just in terms of the species that were being grown, but actually the different forestry management practices between countries. For example, they thin and manage in a different way in Finland compared to Scotland (there is actually very little management in Scotland). The study concluded that in most cases the exploitation cost of trying to detail round poles is a greater effort than it is worth.

Subsequent to this study, there are now other examples of specialist uses for wood which could be beneficial for peripheral regions. A good example is the potential for using very low-grade timber as mass using Spruce. It was invented in Switzerland and beginning with one factory 6 years ago in Southern Germany, there are now 8. There are 2 in Sweden and one in Norway, and I believe there is an ideal opportunity for this to be developed in Scotland. It is a fantastic new technology. By gang-nailing beams together and making them into a slab, you can then pour concrete on it to create timber reinforced concrete. This means replacing steel (which is Co2-using) with timber (which is Co2 storing). Originally, nails were used to hold the wood together, but now hardwood dowels are used. The dowels, made to exactly the same size as the holes they are to be inserted in, are stored in a freezer. They shrink, are inserted into the hole, warm up and expand giving a really tight bond. This is a fantastic technology, but at the moment it has to be imported from Germany or Scandinavia and it is not economically viable. It is very much a local technology, and so I would like to see 2 factories in the Highlands and 4 in the Central Region, within the next 2 years.

Here's an anecdote about the Scottish Parliament. John Kinsley, one of the architects involved, was procuring the windows for the Scottish Parliament. Certain conditions meant that he was required to allow the contractor to source the wood from wherever he chose. The contractor settled for American Oak – it is seen by craftsmen as better to work with. It then went to Indonesia to be made up into a window and it was

Glencoe Visitor Centre, GAIA Architects

then re-exported back to Scotland, and that was supposed to be more economical than actually making it in Scotland. However, at the same time I was involved with a building project in Glencoe, and we were able to procure the wood from within 50 miles of the site to create oak windows for our building. We also investigated the possibility of using local materials for the roof – after all, we no longer have slate in this country, so why should we buy from as far away as Spain for our roofing material? Why not use Scottish timber? So, it is entirely possible to create good quality products from local timber.

During a lecture in Lapland, I was approached by someone who had developed a cellulose insulation material. He was keen to export it to Germany where the biggest market is for this kind of product. However, the glue he was using contained, amongst other things, formaldehyde. I made him aware that this would not be acceptable to the German market, and so he developed a lignum glue, and dramatically demonstrated it's environmental friendliness by tearing off a strip and eating it! This sort of innovation is not currently happening in this country, and because of this ecological buildings remain very expensive. We need this sort of entrepreneurial flair to make these kinds of products more available and affordable.

The next stage of the cycle is how to make a built structure sustainable. By using nails on wooden structures, you cannot take them apart without destroying the wood. A simple solution is to use screws and bolts so that it can be disassembled. For our building in Glencoe, we used Spruce in this manner, and it's perfectly durable. Timber is very good for foundations too - Venice and Amsterdam are founded on timber. Under the water it will last for hundreds of years and above the ground it will last for 100 years. It is only vulnerable when it is subjected to wetting and drying. Timber can be used in surprising ways, and the Scandinavians are particularly good at this, often using it to create ingenious roof designs. We developed a nail-free floor – it is secured with screws and the whole floor can be lifted for maintenance or for recycling. Timber is a great material, but I believe that we should stop using harmful chemicals to treat our wood. These chemicals are often highly toxic and harmful to our health and to the environment. The incidence of asthma in Scottish children has gone up 25% in 3 years, and because we spend 90% of our time indoors we can be

fairly certain that the materials we are using in the indoor environment are contributing to the problem. At the beginning of the last century there were only 50 materials available to the building industry, but now we have over 55,000, of which the vast majority are man-made. In the '60s about 5 of these were above acceptable World Health Organisation levels. By 1984, a study showed that nearly 600 were above the safety levels, and one-third of those were known carcinogens. The situation may well be worse now, and so I advocate leaving timber untreated when it is used indoors. Untreated timber has ideal moisture controlling properties too – it can take in and give off moisture quite freely in a way that man-made materials cannot.

Recycling is the next part in the timber life-cycle. Obviously this is dependent on the longevity of the wood. There are many examples of how untreated wood can last for a long time if used appropriately. In Scandinavia it is very unusual to use treat roofs – it is just a matter of choosing the right type of wood for the purpose. The highest building in Britain, on top of Ben Nevis, has a timber roof, and on the wild west coast of Norway, with all the wind and rain, wood is used in building construction. So wood can be made to last a long time, but eventually it will be recycled in some way. This is not as straightforward as you might assume, since a lot of wood is treated with bitunol or cuprinol which are regarded as low level toxic waste, and so it cannot simply be disgarded or burned. Again, this supports the argument for leaving wood untreated. A study in Norway has looked into the potential for buildings to store CO_2, and has concluded that by only slightly increasing the timber content of their buildings, it would have more impact than if every car in Norway was to change to a completely pollution-free fuel. The reason for this is that trees store a huge amount of CO_2 – every 1 kilogram of wood is equivalent to about 3.6 kilograms of stored CO_2. Therefore, if we start to replace CO_2-hungry building materials with timber, the impact of the building industry's contribution to the CO_2 savings in this country would be considerable. It is very simple – there is no need for expensive eco-technology, such as photovoltaic cells which need replaced after about 25 years. The CO_2 saving is in the very fabric of the building. That is real sustainability.

VERNACULAR USE OF TIMBER

Chris McGregor, Historic Scotland

This morning I would like to go through a series of headings and talk about the North Atlantic tradition by looking at some Scottish examples. I shall look at the traditional Black House as well as other traditional uses of timber in Scotland. I will consider the sources of information about the history of timber use that are available to us and then consider the development of timber in construction and finally finish with a case study of a project that we are currently working on at Sunnybrae.

The North Atlantic tradition:

This is an Icelandic example of a turf house, and I hope you can see that within that there is a timber frame with massive walls. In this tradition the birch bark would form the waterproofing layers over the roof and be taken over the walls as well to protect the inner fabric. In this example, also from Iceland, you can see that they have used peat or turf in these herringbone

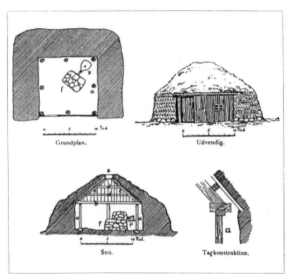

Icelandic Turf

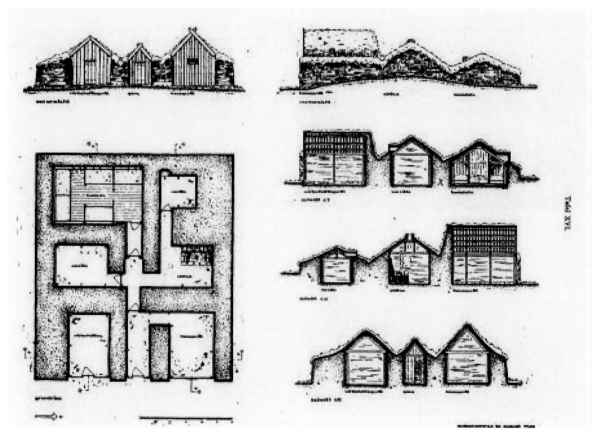

Icelandic Turf House

patterns, which are very common throughout the North Atlantic. The range of patterns that are used for around the door opening or the gable ends are particularly significant but, again, a timber frame within a mass of earthen material. Moving on to Norway, and looking at the traditional dwelling, you can see the traditions here of timber frame within the main dwelling house. The animal quarters would have a cruck frame construction; a well-protected and environmentally sustainable structure.

This is a Scottish structure – somewhat dilapidated – but as a source of information it is quite superb. I would guess it is a timber frame construction, but it is not clear. It demonstrates a wonderful use of second-hand material where they have got re-used timber perhaps from a ship. There is a wonderful use of cabers –a branch has been left on the end of the caber so you hook it over the top vertical horizontal pole giving support for the roof structure all the way through.

Moving on, of course in Scotland the use of the herringbone pattern constructed of peat. Not so much timber used because the sources of timber were not readily available in Uist, peat being used as fuel to heat the house as well.

The traditional Scottish Black House, this one drawn by Captain Thomas, after it was clad with stone. The cladding of stone was an application made really to reduce the maintenance on the structure; the requirement for the workers to actually re-turf on a regular basis, giving a protection of stone actually maintained it for a lot longer. The Black House was made from local materials, built and orientated to take the prevailing weather, kept low and aerodynamically shaped to reduce the risk of damage from storm gales and had a single heat source with privacy partitions, small windows and well insulated. Am I describing a house of the future, or would I be describing a Black House? I think we can learn a great deal from this vernacular position that we have, and it is a wonderful

Scottish structure demonstrating re-use of second-hand material

Turf house showing herringbone pattern common throughout the North Atlantic-South Uist 1886

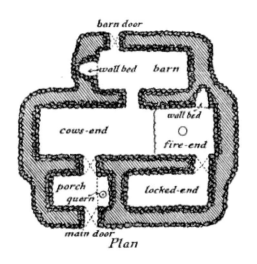

Plan

Scottish Blackhouse

source for sustainable development. The Black House as you know had the animal quarters at one end, and their living quarters at the other. This beautiful shape is a means of smoke control to keep the smoke away from the animals, and to keep it above the level of people living in the house. But timber was very scarce and all sorts of timbers were used in the Black House. We often talk about the 200-yard rule. I think in the Black House we talk about the 5000-mile Gulf Stream rule where timber is washed up from the Gulf Stream and is used in the structure throughout. I will not talk a great deal about vernacular furniture, but there is a wonderful collection at the Highland Folk Museum if anybody's interested in following that up. The Black House had box beds in the best room and the best room, in this case, was entirely wallpapered out, the paper simply pinned to the existing structure. In the main room we have the central hearth, but you need to keep the roof open to allow the smoke to percolate through the turf and through the thatch. In the Black House the waterproofing was done by means of the two layers of turf that were above the cabers. The turf was taken from the peat bog and the combination of oil in the turf and the process of drying, formed a waterproof layer.

You would have a seat over the far side of the room, and you have the dresser. The wallpaper was taken up to a point where the debris from the roof would not fall on the furniture, or would protect you if you were sitting in your seat in the Black House. Timber of course being a scarce material was used and reused, as you can see in the bottom door you have fish boxes put together to form this door; the upper door is formed of timber hinges and beautifully detailed again. Basketwork for carrying the peat. This is a small example. For example in the creel houses which, again, is a strong tradition in Scotland and in the north Atlantic. Basketwork would be used to line the inside of the houses. Hugh Cheap has done a great deal of work on basketwork and he is still researching the subject. The one that I like best is the vernacular coathangers.

I think if you saw it in a Philip Stark catalogue you would think that is was just amazing, it is just such a nice use of timber seeing its potential and using it appropriately. Vernacular timber has been used for a number of uses, for example as horizontal boarded roofing material, as a timber lum and timber boarding above a base course of rubble. The base course of

Furniture - Blackhouse Arnol Isle of Lewis

Interior of Blackhouse showing vernacular coat stand

Gamekeeper's Bothy

rubble can vary in height and the great thing, as you will see with the cruck frame, is that that walling material can be virtually any material you like.

Sources of Information

Here in the picture above we have the cruck frame and the cabers. No drying day, inclement weather outside - the room would be used in different ways to dry the clothes in different seasons. And of course the famous Penny Wedding when the barn would be cleared to celebrate the wedding and you can see the evidence of the timbers obviously round timbers used in the roof. Many painters and their paintings provide valuable sources of information. We have Wilkie showing collections of interiors that tell us a great deal about the

social side and how the house was used, and how people lived in the early 19th century. The other source we have throughout Scotland is the incredible photographic collections that most universities and local authorities have. This is Angus Museum's Collection but as you have seen the Wilson Collection at Aberdeen University and the wonderful collection at St Andrew's University are all incredible sources for looking at traditional vernacular architecture. Moving on perhaps from Hazel bent timber.

A Penny Wedding, David Allan

Search for the Deserter, Hugh Collins 1868

Travelling people Bender Tent

Crucks made up of many small sections of timber, Laidhay Dunbeath Caithness

Again, it is very similar to the Norwegian travelling people's tents, a very similar construction. From bending timber to timber that is already bent. We move on to the cut frame.

Sheep Cot at Coul

This sheep cot at Coul shows a basic cruck frame where the roof cladding material is obviously thatch, but you can see that the cruck itself is earth fast taking any structural loads right down to the ground, therefore the walling material could be anything. In this case, again, it is probably a wattle material or a woven material of some sort which allows, again, for the sheep perhaps – bringing them in just before shearing – plenty of ventilation and shelter to dry off. Again clever use of materials' form and function working beautifully. But crucks can take various shapes and sizes and be developed too as I hope you see.

Crucks can be made up of many small sections of timber, which have been pegged together. The skill is in the pegging and the type of pegging and the offset holes to tighten up these joints and form a structure.

Priorslynn, Canonbie in Dumfriesshire was a Historic Scotland grant case. We are trying to preserve as much of the historic interior as we could in conjunction with the Trust who worked on the project. You can see again the crucks are earth-fast. The tie at mid point

projecting on to take the poles that support the cabers – the horizontal members that will support the vertical cabers. Note the bent pole and as you can imagine, if that was a straight pole taken from the ground your head room in that building would be fairly minimal. The use of bent wood to give you a greater usable space, within the same height restrictions, is quite clever. The fundamental details of the cruck is a bent piece of timber, just as in the shipping industry traditional boatbuilders would look for - nice elbows for specific parts of the boat. The traditional vernacular builder would be out looking for bent branches and in a lot of cases they are simply halved down the middle. This will provide a pair of crucks which are obviously beautifully matched, and we find more often than not, that they are formed in pairs like that, and extended in a variety of ways by pegging on additional timbers to them.

Here, at the National Trust Property at Killin, a beautiful long house with the animals at the far side, and the living quarters with the porch at this side, and you can see under the wonderful crinkly tin, what would have been a timber canopy for the chimney. The chimney on the gable end is obviously a later chimney that has gone in when that would be the best room where the Minister would go and then be entertained. This was surveyed by the Royal Commission and as

National Trust property at Morlanich Killin

you can see at this end you do have the box beds and the kitchen/living room at this end, and then the animals quarters at the other end. These crucks are fairly low timbers, but have been extended in a range of ways to provide sufficient height for the building using horizontal members, vertical king post type arrangements of a whole range of constructions to form this wonderful roof. Still intact and still beautifully maintained.

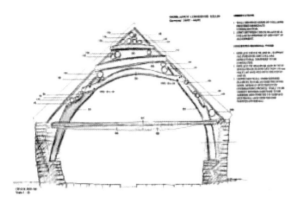

A whole range of constructions still intact and beautifully maintained

Repairs were carried out to these timbers, and the ones that you see in green are the other repair works we carried out on the other crucks. These crucks, as you see again, are raised up on a platform here, which means that … from there on up that wall can be constructed again of any material you wish.

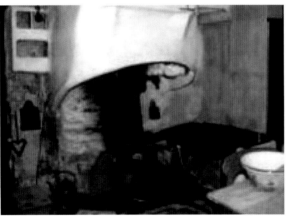

The main fireplace constructed of timber

Inside, this is in the living room with the main fireplace, the main lum, which is formed in timber and made of wallpaper. It is a nice wallpaper lum with about 12 layers of wallpaper over the timber frame and over the mantelpiece as you can see. It forms a piece of sculpture. Within the house itself, most of the rooms have about 8, 10 or 12 layers of wallpaper which gives you a good history of wallpaper as you peel back the

layers, and everything was just papered over. The coat hanger in the hallway had been wall papered over and the paper poked through where the hangers were. It is beautifully constructed. Note the backstone, which is quite interesting as well because with a timber framed lum, you would not want too much heat near your timber. The backstone gives fire protection to the partition. And, again, you would have the bench sitting right next to the hearth where people would sit and tell stories of an evening. You would have a draught screen behind you, which is often referred to as the hallan, to protect the sitting area. Again, traditionally, the cruck and the structure itself would remain the property of the landowner. All the other timber within the building, the tenant would provide, so you were given this empty shell. And you would bring the box beds and the hallan screen, and you would perhaps bring your vernacular furniture into this house.

Earth-fast cruck frame, Priorslynn Canonbie Dumfrieshire

Priorslynn in Canonbie the crucks are single timbers and clay wall construction. It is a slightly more sophisticated construction with the crucks themselves being earth-fast. As Howard said, rock might be a problem, and what you often find is that the foot of the cruck rots away, and the cruck slowly but surely climbs up the wall as you take off the rotten bits, or they replace the base, sometimes with a padstone. It is again a traditional construction.

Jointing at the head of the cruck - Corrimony, Highland

At Corrimony, if I showed you this jointing at the head of the cruck without giving you the background to what I was talking about, you would think this was a quite sophisticated piece of modern technology. The jointing at the head of these crucks is quite superb, and if I had just perhaps left the Royal Commission's illustration on, it would be difficult to say when this dates from. It provides a wonderful space.

At Cromarty the timber is used for ventilation to provide a drying area in the barn. The timber is square, beautifully jointed and built into slots in the wall. This all of course leads on to the sophisticated development of the cruck and into perhaps more architecture than building.

These illustrations from "Innocents" book on the Development of English Building Construction, which could be off-putting for us Scots, but it is a wonderful book and I thoroughly recommend it. It has a wealth of detail in it about Scottish construction.

Case Study

There is a wonderful cottage at the head of Pitlochry, which is under a crinkly roof. We were asked to go and look at this by the local History Society. They thought it was old and quite interesting, but did not quite know what it was. Dr Bruce Walker and I had a look at this house and when we first saw it, you could see it was plasterboard lined as if a modern plasterboard shoebox

Achmae Barn at Stromeferry Cromarty

Sunnybrae Cottage with crinkly roof at Pitlochry, Perthshire

had been slid inside the house. It was difficult to discern anything of great significance. It was agreed that Historic Scotland would acquire this property and take it into care. We wanted to record the property in great detail. I think it is a great move for Historic Scotland to look at the range of properties, not only the grand houses in Scotland, but also some of the traditional houses that ordinary people would be living in. So we eventually took this property into care. We sent a photographer up on the Thursday to take photographs of the house as it was lived in, with all its furniture and everything there so that we had a record. Unfortunately, the removal firm swapped dates with another house, and moved all the furniture out a day ahead of when it was programmed to. So this is what our photographer got, unfortunately.

But with the cooperation of the local History Society we do have some evidence of what was there before, and we will be able to use this when we tell the story of Sunnybrae. What we have been doing is slowly peeling back the layers. You can see that having

Timber lining revealed once the plasterboard was removed

removed the plasterboard, we have this timber lining – again a much later timber lining. The great excitement for us was in the roofspace. When we opened the roof hatch and climbed in, we found that this was in fact a cruck framed cottage made from beautiful ash timber.

The investigations we carried out on this cottage had been quite intensive. As well as our own survey team, we have had consultant archaeologists. Dr Tim Holden has done a great deal of work on the investigation of thatch, archaeologically digging the thatch in the roof. We have also had advice from Dr Ann Crone on dendrochronology to try to establish a date for the ash. Ann is still working on that project, but it is quite exciting. From some of the examples here you can tell something about the construction of these crucks. This cruck was obviously pit sawn. You can see the horizontal cut marks on this. Clearly pit sawn and cut in half, and the main structure of this Ann has been able to deduce from her investigation came from 4 trees; quite a sustainable piece of architecture, I think. But we have been looking at the pegs involved in great detail and other people that we have had involved are our own specialist conservation people looking at the timber, at the wallpaper, giving us advice on the conservation treatment that requires to be carried. We have also had the carpenter "Oak & Woodland" giving us their professional advice on the timbers, and what the background to this structure might be. In searching through the dendrochronology we found that the thinner trees were actually the older trees, so they probably grew on a rocky outcrop where the soil underneath was not of great quality. The rings were very close, which meant that they have lasted extremely well, and so we don't have to do a great deal of work. The Birch cabers are not in the same sort of condition. Some of them are like aerobars that we are

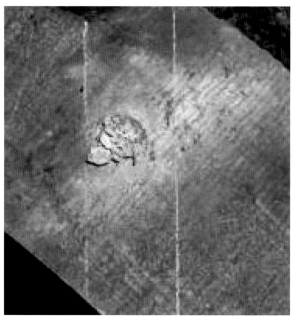

Pit sawn timber showing peg

Cruck frame of ash timber

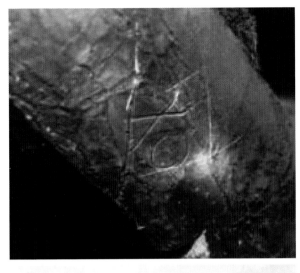

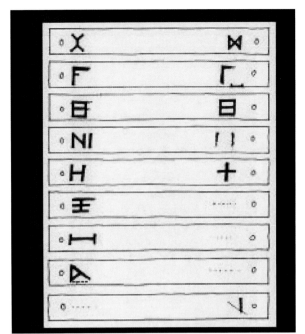

Sunnybrae Timber marks

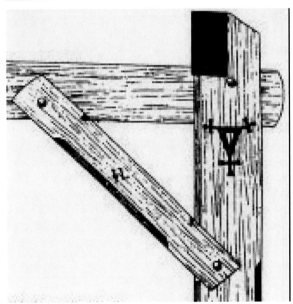

going to have to do some consolidation on, but in the main, we will try and keep this roof very much intact. One thing, which we did find and, again, I would be interested in anybody else that has got information on this, is the timber marks.

On this side are some Norwegian examples of timber marking and timber construction. These are quite extensive, as we know. The ones on the far side are the timber marks that we have at Sunnybrae Cottage. Again, whether they are someone going to the sawmill and saying these are mine, and putting their mark on them, or whether they have got them from the forest and said to the owners that these are my timbers and set them aside for me, we are still not clear. But it would be very useful to have some discussion on that. We know exactly what the tools were to form these, and these are formed on the back. These are not formed on the timber, so they must have been done somewhere fairly close to the source. Our archaeologists are continuing to peel back the layers and look at the cottage in great detail. The brick chimney, which was in position in the top slide here, clearly a later insertion. We had a lum, maybe not a paper lum, but certainly a basketwork lum with clay on either side, formed at this end of the house. The chimney at that end is a dummy

Norwegian examples of timber markings

chimney and like the chimney at the other end was a later insertion, when that became the best room in the house. The archaeology has been extremely worthwhile and the research work on that is continuing and we are just about to start another campaign of work on the cottage. We think we will be telling the story of the archaeology of this cottage and we have been speaking to our colleagues in the National Trust to link with places like Morlanich and tell stories in that way, rather than do some sort of reconstruction within this house. But that is very much an ongoing project that we are working on as I speak. What we have also been doing is looking at early forms of construction.

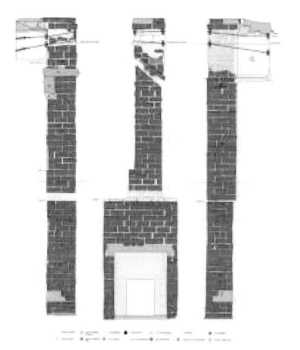

Archaeological investigations at Sunnybrae

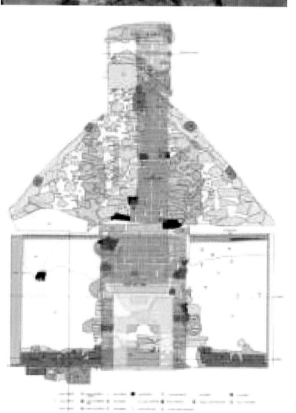

In fact my last slide is a conjectural reconstruction of what the cottage may have started off as, which brings us right back to the North Atlantic connection, the Seasamie houses or the creel houses if you like. This might have been perhaps what it was. Again, as I said, the wall construction could be of any material. It is not load-bearing at all. It may have had a basketwork interior as was shown here on the plan.

Just to finish, I would like to thank the Royal Commission for the slides that they lent me and Geoffrey Stell who also lent me slides for this presentation. Also, I would like to thank the consultancy team who has been working at Sunnybrae. I'd like to thank Bruce Walker who has done lots of work on timber construction in vernacular construction in Scotland.

TIMBER IN SCOTTISH HISTORIC BUILDINGS

Geoffrey Stell

This overview of the use of timber in Scottish historic buildings of formal, supra-vernacular status takes us to the top of the tree in metaphorical social terms and, in material terms, to the best cuts of timber. The patrons of the buildings under review here - from the Crown, Nobility and Church downwards - have been in a position to use the best of what is locally available or to afford a wider choice of imported timber. For although medieval and later Scotland had plentiful indigenous woodlands, building accounts show that even by the later Middle Ages 'Eastland boards', other forms of softwood and even hardwoods were being imported from Scandinavia and the Baltic region. As Robert Edward, a well-informed commentator on Angus put it in 1678, 'for the houses in the towns, and those of gentlemen in the country, timber is brought from Norway; not because Scotland does not afford wood sufficient to supply the whole kingdom, but because rugged and impassable rocks prevent it being transported from those places where it grows.'

Whilst they may not bear comparison with the carpentry traditions of England, features of timber construction which have endured in Scotland show a much greater range and variety than is generally recognised, and the one-time timber profile is enhanced by innumerable roofless and floorless ruins. Excavation sites are constantly revealing evidence of timber-built structures, including important buildings such as halls, not just those of subordinate, ancillary purpose. The lengths and spans of many stone buildings, such as Morton Castle, also clearly reflect the use of substantial timbers, in this case from Nithsdale, a valley whose clay soils have long been an important source of oak trees.

However, timber building in Scotland is by no means a lost world of materials and traditions that have long since vanished. A suitable starting-point to demonstrate that this is far from the case is provided by one of the late 16th-century maps of Timothy Pont, that for Moray and Nairn, which depicts a well-wooded landscape of deciduous trees around Darnaway Castle, an area of royal forest to the west of Forres. This is known to have been a significant source of timber over many

centuries, particularly during the reign of King James IV (1488-1513), when Darnaway contributed to a number of major royal building ventures. Though the forest at Darnaway could not be described as 'vast', its sessile oaks were clearly of an eminently usable quality and, importantly, were also accessible, via the nearby River Findhorn, which allowed them to be transported by water to the coast and thence to the south. Symbolised on the Pont map, probably fairly accurately, Darnaway Castle, an early royal hunting lodge associated later with the earls of Moray, stands at the edge of one area of woodland. Given its ancient forest setting, it is fitting that Darnaway still retains what is probably the earliest and most complete medieval timber roof in Scotland.

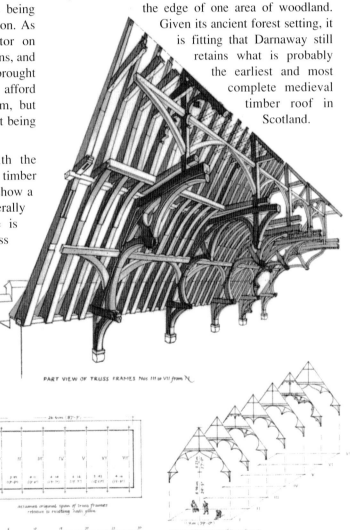

PART VIEW OF TRUSS FRAMES Nos III to VII from N.

Darnaway Castle, Moray: plan and perspective part view of roof over great hall; drawing by Geoffrey Hay.

In the early 19th century Darnaway was transformed from a medieval castle into a Georgian mansion by the 9th Earl of Moray. This scheme, which was completed in 1812, was carefully undertaken in a way which preserved and, in modem parlance, 'showcased' the medieval great hall and its magnificent roof which, even at that date, was regarded as a precious object of venerable antiquity. The roof had long been assumed to have been of late medieval origin, possibly dating from one of the documented episodes of building in the middle and later 15th century, so upon becoming accessible for close-range survey in 1987, when the upper part of the hall was being redecorated, Moray Estates seized the opportunity for tree-ring analysis. From this dendrochronological dating exercise, a very good representative set of twelve oak timbers made a perfect match with the Scottish chronology and pointed conclusively to a felling date of around 1387. Given that oak must be worked whilst it is green and before it hardens, the timbers of the Damaway roof are thus likely to have been assembled and placed in position not long after that date.

With an overall length of almost 27 m and a clear span of nearly 11m, Darnaway is close in scale to its royal descendants over the great halls at Stirling and Edinburgh. These are its nearest - indeed its only known - Scottish parallels in general appearance and hammer-beam style. In their original incarnations, both these royal roofs were put up in the reign of James IV in the early 16th century, more than four generations after Darnaway. Even in England, the hammer-beam genre, an alternative means of spanning halls that would otherwise have been aisled, had not yet reached its apogee by 1387, though it did so in style in the following decade in the shape of the reconstructed Westminster Hall, a roof which, for the record, is twice the span of Damaway and three times the length.

The relatively steeply-pitched Darnaway roof is essentially a two-tier structure, each truss being made up of a triangular upper stage with double collars and a lower stage of truncated arch-braced collar beam form, each stage evidently being of independent construction but sharing the system of purlins. It is of hammer-beam type but, lacking vertical hammer posts above the lower horizontal members, it has come to be regarded by technical purists as a 'false' hammer-beam roof. However, it is fair to say that the way the structure actually works in the vital area of the wall-head, where much remains invisible, is still a little unclear. The main members of a pair of trusses are more ornately carved and cusped than the rest, probably serving as spere trusses delimiting the dais or high table area. Detailed decoration is everywhere, for there is a whole world of human figures, beasts, birds and naturalistic carvings inhabiting this roof. Many of them evoke the atmosphere and spirit of the wild

Darnaway Castle, Moray: specimen pendant post in roof over great hall.

forest, such as the bear-like creatures on the ends of the pendant posts and a hunting scene carved in relief on the soffit of one of the beam-ends.

The truncated arch-braced form with pendant posts which makes up the lower part of the Damaway roof was echoed in two, much later roofs by the master wright, John Scott. One is the flattish, five-arched roof of Danish oak over the Parliament House in the Law Courts complex in Edinburgh, completed in 1639. The other is a near-contemporary roof of steeper, six-arch profile over the Tron Church, lower down the High Street in Edinburgh.

Medieval hall and tower roofs would generally have been of lesser span, complexity and decoration than these grand examples. They were impressive nonetheless, as the example of the hall of the town house of the Knights Hospitallers in Linlithgow demonstrated. Unfortunately, this building was demolished in 1883 but not before it - and its roof - were thoroughly surveyed and measured. Probably dating from about 1500, the architectural detailing bears close similarities to the nearby royal palace. The roof, which was evidently of oak, was of an arch-braced double collar truss form with wind braces at the heads and sides. The overall span was relatively modest, less than 5.5 metres, but the overall effect was undeniably grand. The timber may well have come from nearby Torphichen, the main centre for the Hospitallers in Scotland and from where Edward I is known to have used oaks for the building of his peel at Linlithgow a couple of centuries earlier.

Scotland has no medieval timber church-building tradition, either of the Norwegian or English regional varieties, and even surviving medieval church roofs are quite scarce. The earliest surviving examples are a few component parts of 13th-century scissor trusses over the choir and nave of Glasgow Cathedral. They are similar in general form to the late medieval roof of about 1500 which covered the refectory range of Ardchattan Priory in Argyll, of which again only portions still survive. Probably the most complete surviving medieval church roof in Scotland is that over the nave of the Church of the Holy Rude, Stirling, which may date from about 1470. It is of tie beam and king post construction, each principal rafter being of double or flitched form trapping the through purlins and below each tie-beam there is an extended wall-post and arched brace. At least one other major burgh church, St John's, Perth, retains parts of a tie-beam roof of broadly analogous form, but just how typical these were is hard to say. The indications are that, from the later Middle Ages into the 18th century, the majority of the roofs over Scottish churches, towers and houses were of much simpler, closely spaced common rafter form.

There were, however, many variations on the collar-rafter roof theme. The double collar-rafter roof which covered the main block of the late 15th-century Inverquharity Castle, for example, supported a roof covering of heavy stone slates characteristic of Angus,

so the rafters are superimposed by open battens, to which the slates are pegged, they are very closely spaced, and the undersides of the lower collars are braced. In many other parts of the country, the groundwork for the roof covering was formed by close-butted or close-jointed sarking boards, to which the slates were nailed, and which, in the absence of purlins, also provided some lateral rigidity. An ubiquitous, almost standard, feature of late medieval and early modem roofs of this type is the triangulated ashlaring at the wall head. In contrast to earlier roofs, Scats practice came to favour the setting of the vertical ashlar posts in front of the horizontal sole-piece, sometimes continuing down and helping to grip the wall. Many also bore carpenters' assembly marks, usually but not invariably incised in the form of Roman numerals and usually on each member of a single roof frame. Out of sequence, they may serve as tell-tale indicators of subsequent dismantling and re-assembly.

Another variation on the collar-rafter theme, still seen, for example, in the surviving aisle of Guthrie Collegiate Church (1464) and Bardowie Castle (1566) involves the use of stilted or curved arch braces beneath the collars, almost certainly intended to serve as the underside or formwork for a boarded ceiling of mock barrel-vaulted form of the kind found at Culross Palace, Fife, where the timber barrel vault bears tempera-painted decoration.

Bardowie Castle, Stirlingshire (now East Dunbartonshire): arch-braced collar-rafter roof over main block.

Many Scottish houses of the later medieval and early modem periods are made up of, assemblages of adjacent buildings, jambs or wings, and turrets. Accordingly, their upperworks and roofs reflect many variations in layout, including the famous set of alphabetical (L, T, Z) plan configurations. However, contrary to popular belief, the saddles and swept valleys which join up adjacent tower roofs, so beloved of modem restorers, are almost invariably late modifications of 18th century or later date as was once the case of this Galloway tower (Barscobe) of 1648. All the available evidence points to an original separation of adjacent roofs and the extensive use of intermediate or valley gutters, no doubt lined with much sheet lead. In this particular case, the subsidiary roof over the stair wing was originally separate, gabled on the inner as well as the external face, but subsequently extended on a system of inter-connecting jack-rafters to meet the roof over the main block.

Timber-framed houses are conspicuous by their absence from the Scottish countryside. This cultural gap in part reflects differences in the make-up of the country's social and tenurial structure, given that Scotland lacked a substantial tenant or yeoman freeholder class, builders of so many of the half-timbered houses in England and Wales. However, in Scottish towns, as elsewhere in Europe, timber construction remained the norm for many centuries. Indeed, despite increasing reliance on timber imports, late 16th-century Edinburgh witnessed a noticeable resurgence in building houses almost completely of timber on a substantial and expensive scale, possibly a result of foreign fashion, from the direction of the Hanseatic towns. Almost entirely timber-framed and jettied buildings of this kind - evidently with masonry walling only at ground-level and party walls - used to stand in the Lawnmarket, including one at the head of the West Bow which was demolished in 1878. Across the street in the terrace which still includes Gladstone's Land there was another of the same type dated 1580 which was demolished in 1883. Above the ground-floor walls, the frontage of this building was wholly timber-framed and the cantilever-posts were formed by a series of main beams. Moreover, in a small portion above the pend, it was timber-framed and jettied at the back as well as the front - the only recorded case of this kind in Scotland.

Scotland's timber skyscrapers were regularly commented upon by visitors in the 17th century, some noting that many of the houses were actually stone-built structures with only the frontages or galleries of timber. The restored timber frontage of the so-called John Knox's House, for example, which dates originally from about 1570, and is jettied in two stages, has small foregalleries or forestairs set wholly in front of a load-bearing stone wall and the openings within

are specifically designed for them - with fireplaces, doorways and passages all along one side. Next door is Moubray House and within its roof-space a timber barrel vault, lined with painted pine boarding of about 1600, was uncovered during restoration work. In the original framework of the front-wall a later sash window broke up an original triple window - or three-light strip window - the right-hand opening still preserving an inward-opening two-leaf shutter, but with no evidence of glazing. It must qualify as one of the earliest surviving domestic windows in Edinburgh.

One of the most complete specimens of such timber-fronted houses with relatively un-restored timberwork used to stand in the Watergate, Perth, until 1966 when this early 17th-century building, evidently the town house of the 1st Earl of Kinnoull, was demolished. It was a three-storeyed building, approximately square on plan with a circular stair-tower projecting into the street at one angle. A galleried timber frontage ran the length of the street elevation and partly encased the stair-tower. The framing covered the upper two storeys and was of independent construction at each level. Most of the original studs survived in situ, as did three original mid-rails which appeared to be the sub-frames for window-openings. Grooves in the associated sill-beams pointed to an earlier form of panel infill, probably of timber boards or wattle. The timber was of oak throughout.

A French tradition surrounding timber-framed town houses has redounded somewhat unexpectedly to Scotland's credit. The town of Aubigny-sur-Nere in the departement of Cher in Central France is particularly proud of the Scottish origins of its one-time lords, the Stuarts of Aubigny, and the part that they played in the struggle for the liberation of the French kingdom after 1419. In 1512 an extensive tire, which started by accident, destroyed much of Aubigny, but the houses were soon rebuilt thanks to the generosity of Robert Stuart, who permitted extensive use of timber from the nearby forests on his estate. Luckily, fire did not strike again, and modem Aubigny retains a remarkably homogeneous group of timber-framed town houses built in the space of a generation between 1513 and 1543. Many of their timber frontages bear decorative cross-braces which are invariably referred to as the cross of St Andrew. Persistent tradition interprets this architectural signature as a deliberate tribute to the Stuart seigneur, even though it is also recognised that the saltire-shaped cross-brace is also commonly found on town houses in Bourges and elsewhere in that region. Now usually masonry-encased rather than externally framed, Scotland's multi-storeyed tenement-buildings constitute a distinctive urban house-type which is of a form not shared with other countries of the British Isles, being found here long before the era of mass industrial housing in the 18th, 19th and 20th

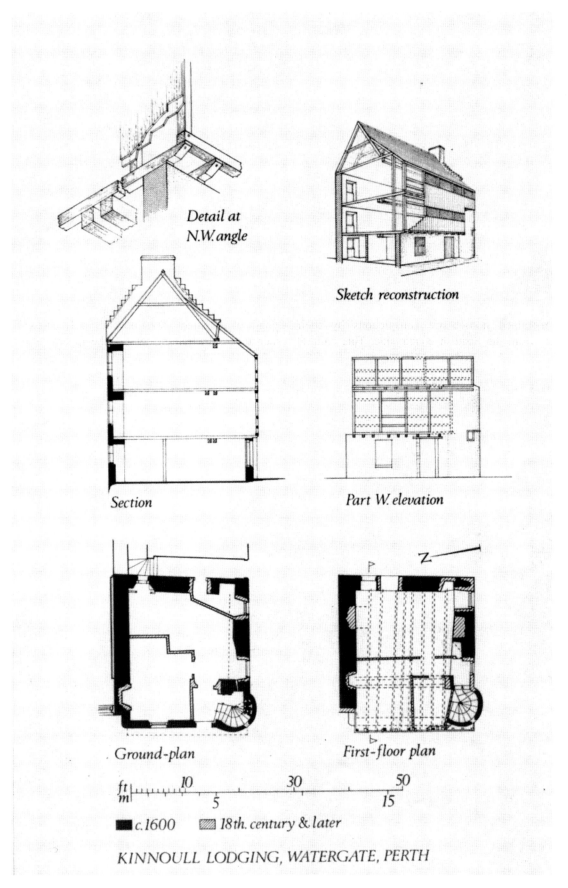

Detail at N.W. angle

Sketch reconstruction

Section

Part W. elevation

Ground-plan

First-floor plan

ft
m
10   30   50
5   15

■ c.1600   ▨ 18th. century & later

KINNOULL LODGING, WATERGATE, PERTH

Kimroull Lodging, Watergate, Perth: plans, section, elevation, detail and reconstruction drawing.

334-40 Lawnmarket, Edinburgh: timber-framed building drawn by James Drummond, 1852.

centuries. A hidden but significant feature of their construction is the internal timber framing and flooring required over several storeys. Detailed survey of a typical Edinburgh tenement of the second quarter of the 18th century has revealed a framed system of main beams and vertical posts, all evidently of pine, carried over four storeys. The beams, which serve as the basis for lath-and-plaster partitions, were made up of scarf-jointed lengths, jointed over the junctions with the vertical posts which, for structural reasons, were staggered in relation to each other.

Many early floors were of double- or triple-tiered construction, analogous in strength and flexibility with those designed for later industrial buildings with moving loads. This form of flooring usually incorporates a pair of runner beams carried on corbels along the side-walls; these runners support the main joists which are in turn notched to receive short transverse filler-joists. The positions of the corbels may or may not correspond with the ends of the main joists. Wider spans would probably have had central rows of posts which were set on padstones and carried longitudinal or spine beams.

One hidden but structurally important use of timber in Scottish historic buildings resides in its application as a foundation material. Vertically-set piles and horizontal grids or frameworks of timber, known as branders, sometimes rubble-filled (when they were known as starlings), were commonly used in river bridge foundations, particularly in tidal rivers. It is less widely recognised that similar substructures were also used for buildings founded on light and sandy soils (like the massive late medieval bishop's castle in the centre of Dornoch) or on boggy ground. In Scotland this technique is most famously represented by King's College, Aberdeen, founded in 1505. There, as a mid-17th-century topographical account makes clear, 'the foundation of the whole structure, as it rests on yielding and wet soil, was laid on oak beams at great expense and trouble'. However, unlike Winchester Cathedral which had similar watery foundations set on beech logs, there has yet been no occasion to send down a diver below any Scottish building in order to investigate signs of structural failure and any changes in the underlying water table.

Finally, while timber as applied to Scottish industrial and engineering structures is a vast subject, in a conference on this theme it is appropriate to draw particular attention to structures associated with the charcoal phase of the iron industry in the West Highlands, well exemplified by the mid-18th century ironworks at Bonawe, Argyll, in the care of Historic Scotland. Given the difficulties of transporting the friable charcoal, it was the presence of woodlands for the production of charcoal, rather than of iron ore, that determined the siting of such blast furnaces in the Highlands where the huge timber requirements could be adequately met. Storage of the precious charcoal was obviously a matter of high priority, probably, as in Sweden, originally in low timber buildings, but subsequently, in the later 18th century as the state of business permitted the investment, it came to be stacked on wooden racks in spacious, well-ventilated barn-like 'coal houses', as they were called. At Bonawe, they have central aisles of more than six-metre span covered with open timber roofs of accomplished tie-beam construction and king-post form.

Storage and drying associated with the brick and tile industry produced timber buildings of a much less grand kind, such as the three-aisled drying shed formerly associated with the Blackpots Brick and Tile Works at Whitehills near Banff Over 71 metres in overall length the shed was of simple post-and-lintel construction, the timber drying racks inside governing the bay modules and the louvring. A wall-plate made up of scarf-jointed sections was supported on masonry piers at the angles and centre, and in each bay it was spiked to timber posts set on padstones. Over the years the structure had settled unevenly, and the undulating profile of the wall-plate and raking louvre props gave the building a decidedly vernacular, if not animated centipedal quality.

Bonawe Ironworks, Argyll: roof over eastern charcoal shed.

Timber structures of a more formal, engineered design were associated with the early Scottish railways. They range from overall timber roofs, now almost entirely removed, to simple, timber-clad, weatherboarded station-buildings. Such structures are now accepted almost as manifestations of regional building traditions, particularly in those parts of North and North-eastern Scotland served prior to 1923 by the former Highland and Great North of Scotland Railways. Paralleling developments on the American railroads, the Scottish railways also became heir to a timber or timber-and-stone bridge-building tradition which has an ancient, medieval ancestry. The Scottish railway network has included wooden trestle bridges carried on stone piers, as was formerly the case with a bridge of wooden cantilever type at Stirling, while at Aultnaslanach on the line between Inverness and Aviemore, opened by the Highland Railway in 1897, is a trestle viaduct composed entirely of pitch-pine baulks with iron-clad joints, the last of its type on a main line in Britain, It owes its survival to the fact that its foundations were considered to be better suited to the surrounding boggy ground than those of a heavier bridge of metal or masonry. Scaffolded for many years,

Huntly, Aberdeenshire: railway station offices.

it is soon to be replaced and literally side-lined alongside its successor.

Aultnaslanach has, however, been thoroughly recorded by RCAHMS and such records are there to be used, both in academic and practical terms. Together, those timber buildings which still endure and remain part of our heritage and those which we have lost but have recorded, constitute a great repertoire which have the potential to inform, inspire and shape new designs in timber from old. The heritage record is a rich and varied resource from which Scotland's buildings of the future can derive great benefit.

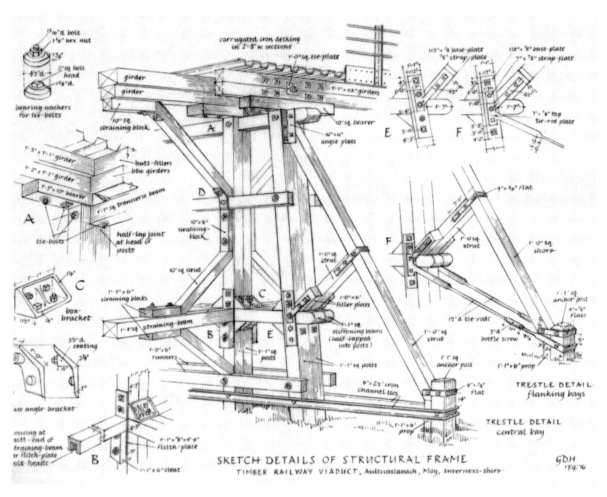

Aultnaslanach Viaduct, Moy, Inverness-shire (now Highland): sketch details of structural frame.

TIMBER ENGINEERING IN A HERITAGE CONTEXT

Robert Bowles, Alan Baxter & Associates

In preparing for speaking to you this morning, I really looked through all the experience I have had over my career in encountering timber in all sorts of different ways in historic buildings. Timber has been used as a building material from the earliest times and in the UK it is really very rare to find a building of any age that does not have timber in it somewhere, and even those which do not have it at the moment, we can be fairly sure that it was used extensively in the construction process. We are all familiar with magnificent examples of pure timber structures, but these are the exception rather than the rule, I find, with historic buildings and most of the structural timber is often out of sight, either because it is inaccessible in a roof space, or because it has been deliberately hidden behind architectural finishes, and whilst there are many buildings which are completely timber framed, on the whole, the timber forms just part of the structure, and it is combined with other materials. And the engineering interest often services from the way that these were combined wisely, or in some case, unwisely, and I found that it is essential to understand the overall structure and form of the building as a whole, before attempting to deal with the timber elements and to have a good understanding of how the whole thing behaves, rather than just the timber elements. The joints are a very critical part of any timber structure, and often the size of the members is determined by the joint's design, and assuming that a ? structure was adequate in the first place, when it was first constructed, I am quite convinced that they will last indefinitely, if they are properly maintained, and if people don't do unwise things to them during the course of their life. I hope the slides have now been changed.

Well I start with a magnificent example, which has already been mentioned, of Westminster Hall, which has been there since the end of the 14th century, and has hardly changed over the years, except that actually in the 1920s the structure, the way it worked, was greatly changed by the insertion of quite a lot of steelwork due to the action of Death Watch beetle and other rot and that sort of thing. But it still looks the same, but perhaps we come more commonly to more vernacular buildings like this, which is a timber-framed house or even that one; and I am not talking about the one with the gable, but the little red K1 telephone box which is Listed in its own right, a timber building, and that possibly is the smallest historic building in the

country that has timber in it. There is a range of timber in all sorts of buildings. Onto a few real engineering examples. This is the end of a beam in a roof in an agricultural building, and the beam end was rotten, and it has been cut away, and we are repairing it. The rotten section has been cut away, a steel splice has been placed in the middle, it has been bolted through and we are awaiting the ? timber pieces to go over there, and then those bolt holes will be plugged by timber and it will end up looking pretty much as it would have done originally, and we have conserved the use of that timber beam. Very easy to have written an engineering report saying that that piece of roof had had it, but it hasn't. If the original designers had detailed it perhaps slightly better, then it might not have got rotten in the end there. Who better to look to for wise detailing than Christopher Wren, who knew about rotten beam ends or the risk of it, and in the roof of St Paul's Cathedral, that is too small there for you to see, but I have got a larger version here, if you look at the right hand of the two sections, this is actually a comparison of Old St Paul's and the present building, but up at the top there the detail of the ends of the roof trusses – he was a bit lucky because he had rather thick walls but – the roof trusses are supported on an inner wall, and the gutter which of course is always the problem, is set down at a lower level so that when it leaks, which it does, all the water and any rotten timbers that occur are just in that little bit which can be replaced and the end of the roof truss is safe and sound. So if you do your detailing properly, and maintain your buildings right, that definitely proves that things last almost indefinitely.

Here is another barn building, which looks rather as if it has seen better days, and indeed when the roof coverings came off, perhaps value engineering had been taken to extremes here in re-sizing some of these members, but it again would have been quite easy to write an engineering report saying that this has really had it, but the building was Listed at Grade 2, part of a group of farm buildings with its group value, and so it was to stay. The approach taken was simply to look at and analyse the framing of what was there, identify its inadequacies, and simply add new members which are in slightly different coloured timber here, to base the thing up, they are reversible, interpretable, and wholly in line with good conservation practice, but they enabled the original timbers to remain there, and the building to take on a new lease of life, and so there was a principle there of taking what was there and adding to it, and similarly I mentioned joints as being the Achilles Heel very often, a helping hand to timber joints can often extend the life of them quite significantly. Here, again, deliberately interpretable and obvious are those 20th-century additions. Here is an example – what comes across very commonly – this is looking upwards at the underside of a timber floor in a house that has been converted to offices. 18th century building, main beam there and the floor joists coming in at the sides. Converted and modernised and central heating and this beam had shrunk, just a little bit – it wasn't rotten, there wasn't anything wrong with it – but it had shrunk, and the original carpenter had set the timbers out so that the frame was tight, as originally constructed, and when the beam shrunk, just a little bit, all the joists then started to come out of their bearings a little bit, and in here a low-key whelping hand – some metal framing anchors, little silvery grey pieces there are each joist – just to give it a helping hand, interpretable and indeed, reversible. Here is a slight step further up the scale of intervention. This is a view on the top of a beam. That's the beam – not looking as you might ordinarily expect, because it has all those black things sticking up out of it, but the issue here was one of deflection of this timber floor and live load, and in particular, there was quite an important painted ceiling underneath, and the concern was that the vibration and movement of the floor was, in the long term, going to threaten this ceiling. And so this was a way that we devised of stiffening that timber beam without sawing into it, without replacing it with steel channels and that sort of thing – which would also have been completely impracticable, given that the ceiling had to be kept – and what we found was that if we made a steel plate – and there it is, with lots of holes in it, and put lots of timber connectors into the beam and put the plate on there – that is going to happen the next day, the day after this photograph was taken, we were able to show you that the stiffness of that beam was actually doubled by doing that. It is not the most efficient use of steel in theory, but that was not the issue. The issue was to in a non minimum intervention thing to stiffen the beam, and so if you want to double the thickness of a timber beam like that, stick a plate on the top, and we did test it in a prime example it did not have a special ceiling underneath it. One sometimes gets surprised in timber structures, and this is one that I often quote is that walls can span. Most people think timber walls are just sitting one on top of the other, but there can be trusses hidden away inside walls. Somebody once accused me of just looking at books to find that, but there is a real example. And if someone I dealing with a building like this, and they don't do their research properly, there have been cases – the proportions of this are reasonably amenable to forming door openings – but I have, on a couple of occasions

where the later M'Lady of the house has insisted on the double door like her neighbour, and they have gone right through that tie up there and then wondered why the whole thing has started to sag, so one has to do one's research and understand exactly what you are dealing with – looking for surprises. Historic buildings come right up to Post War listing as I can see, and there is a fairly industrial sort of scene of a warehouse and granary in London, which we don't get our corn quite like that anymore, and it now looks like that, and it has got the very nice, very expensive flats inside with excellent views of Tower Bridge, but the whole point about the inside of this building was that it had timber floors with timber floorboards and timber joists visible, and beams visible, and cast-iron columns and yet it was such a size that any glance at the building regulations would show that it looked as though the lot would have to be covered up for fire and all those sorts of reasons. But that would indeed destroy the whole point of creating flats of a particular type in this sort of building. So here, what we managed to do was to develop, put a very thin layer of reinforced concrete on top, because the warehouse floors were quite strong enough to carry a bit of dead weight of concrete, but they were not fire-rateable, yet the geometry did not permit to put a fully full thickness of reinforced concrete on top such as would comply with modern codes of practice. So this solution involved reaching for some more seldom used codes of practice which are just full of performance of concrete in fire where for a short time you are allowed to take to overload it, to distort, and so on in ways that it would not otherwise be allowed to do. So, by putting that sort of analysis to this construction, we provided a justification whereby in the long term, the concrete was held up by the timber, but if there was a fire, for the relevant 24 hours after the fire, the concrete would stand on its own, possibly not for longer than that, but that was all the regulations required you to demonstrate and well not necessarily my taste in interior design, but it did enable the whole thing to be converted with the exposed hairy timbers even getting 2 hour fire ratings. So this historic timber structure was allowed to remain on view. Some shoring there, I hope you can see. This is an example of timber that, again, had not decayed, and wasn't even visible, because those are brick-fronted houses, but they were built, not a generation – probably two generations after the Fire of London – and old practices die hard, and there was a lot more timber built into those outside walls than one would think was actually necessary. But I am sure that was the tradition, that they built timber frames and then stuck the bricks round them afterwards, and the issue that had come about here is illustrated by this slide, it was a painting contract; the window frames were being painted by painters suspended in boats down the front of the building, and one Friday evening, I think it was, the lad had been allowed to do some painting, and some paint had got onto the brickwork. The foreman had said well what we have to do about that is wait until that's dry, and on Monday we can start trying to get it off. If we start trying to get it off while it is wet, that's no good. When he came back on Monday, somebody sharp-eyed spotted that the paint had gone and there was a sort of strip of brickwork here that really had no explanation to it. And what had happened over the weekend was that this brick skin had actually pinged out by an inch and a bit and that led the District Surveyor insisting on that scaffolding shoring it up. On investigation, what we actually found was that you could just about see it here, was that almost – this is the front wall when the brick skin had been taken off – half brick skin on the outside. Very, very few header bricks connecting the outer skin into the rest of the construction. An enormous ??? through here, but which was perfectly sound. No rot anywhere, but inside the temperature was about 70 degrees – that is on a bad day – because the secretaries were all sitting there virtually in their bikinis, and it had got incredibly dry and I am quite convinced that what had happened was that this enormous timber had shrunk, without rotting. The piers, the inner part of the pier, which you see there, was actually sitting with the beams sandwiched in the middle of it, and in the shortening, it had put forces into the half brick skin which was just on the outside, and the action of the painters boats clanking down the front, had just been the straw that broke the camel's back and with only one or two headers every square metre, the skin had come loose.

So there is the timber affecting something completely unrelated to timber, and causing distress in the brickwork, but here, again, it was possible to conserve it because the back pier, the backing of the pier was perfectly sound, the timber was sound, and I am afraid all we did was put the half brick skin back, but with lots of stainless steel ties this time instead of just only a few.

Just a couple of further observations. We have seen that timber is used in foundations and it is generally recognised that provided the water content and the anaerobic conditions under which they were almost certainly originally installed, provided that is maintained, then things should go on well forever. But sometimes things change, and the water contents change. The aerial photo of the Palace of Westminster I have put in because I am going to show you about some timber piles that used to be there, and aren't any more, but the point of the photo is really just to say that a good half of the building is built on reclaimed land, and that the natural river edge is probably somewhere about there, and the second thing to say is that it was built in an estuary of a tributary of the Thames that used to come in that way, and so, historically, it was

really quite a marshy place – which is why Westminster Abbey is where it is, because the monks wanted to be somewhere separate, so they chose this gravely delta, much cut about with water courses. But over the years, of course, everything has dried out a bit. This is a simple plan diagram of the Palace. There is the new river wall, new in 1840. The wavy blue line is about the halfway line across that I was referring to in the previous slide, and the red shaded area is the surviving part of the medieval Palace of Westminster.

The public's perception is that apart from Westminster Hall, the whole place was rebuilt after the Fire of 1832. The reality is that there is a couple of bits – there is a cloister there and the undercroft of St Steven's Hall there, the crypt, was kept, and that is an area that we had some interest some 10 years ago when some rather alarming discoveries were made. This is a cross section drawing of the Crypt and Chapel, as it was originally at about that date when, we are reliably sure, the water level the water table was around that sort of level, the floor of the Crypt was well up out of the water to keep the feet dry, and the foundations came down more or less to the water table and at that point, bear in mind we are in very silty material on top of gravel, this is very, very almost like riverside mud, really at the time it was constructed – and timber piles and very sort of normal medieval construction on difficult ground.

After the Fire in 1832, the upper part of the Chapel was actually taken down completely but this part was retained and incorporated into the new building. This is slightly two slides put on top of one to speed things up, but the main changes that had taken place, apart from the new superstructure up here, was that the floor was more or less at the same level, but an undercroft had been created between the original foundations. And this was a very good source of distribution for the heating mains. Also, of course, the river wall reclaimed into the river was an extraordinarily effective water barrier, and then they came along and dug the underground railways on the landward side which acted as a cut off drain from the river, the tributary river, and the whole of this silty material under here did dry out, over a period of probably 100 years or so, because it was not until 1990 that some investigations were going on down here, and some quite alarming holes were found under the foundation here because, not only had the timber piles rotted away, but the actual whole material under here in drying out had shrunk quite a bit, and the water table was down there. It is rather difficult to photograph a hall, but that's a biro, to give you the scale, so you could look along here, and if I had been a mouse I could have gone quite a long way under there, quite happily because this material had shrunk away, and the timber piles had rotted away. But we knew quite conclusively that those timber piles were perfectly all right in 1840 when this was reconstructed, because there was Victorian concrete with the negative impression of the ? caps very clearly on the underside of it. But all there was was a circular hole in the ground which you could sort of go down 4 or 5 ft. Needless to say, that was something that could not be allowed to continue and so, a solution was devised, and there it is, and there were some grouted mini piles – concrete this time – and underpins, where the whole construction was underpinned, and then every time we found a hole in the ground, we filled it full of grout just to fill it up. So when people talk about that timber piles, and it is important to keep the water table where it is. It is, because that's what happens when you don't. Equally, one of the other speakers was talking about drillage foundations, and we have an example of that.

This building is further up Whitehall. This is the original Admiralty Building. You see the Hornblower films on TV, it is where Hornblower goes to get his instructions, which is quite authentic, because that's where it was, and that's where Nelson's body lay the night before his funeral. It has now been refurbished, but this is a very curious building to me, as an engineer, coming to look at it to refurbish it. The superstructure was a very very high quality. The brickwork was absolutely impeccable. The beams, the niches for the floor beams behind there had little arches over the top of them. Absolutely perfect. It was pointed on the inside behind the panelling, very very high quality and yet it was all over the shop, it settling in a most peculiar way, and tilting all over the place, and so some investigations were called for. There was a sort of folklore of, oh there is timber down there in the ground but, eventually, after quite a lot of investigation, a diagrammatic cross section, we were able to determine that the building, again, been the victim of a lowered water table as a result of man's activity and that the original construction had been one of these case where it was built on a timber grillage. But we managed to find out the pattern of this drillage and the sequence of this construction; two longitudinal planks and then some cross beams there, and then the masonry had been built off it. And the problem with the thing drying out was again twofold, that we had gone from a situation there where the ground was evenly loaded, that red represents the intensity of loading, and it was evenly loaded, then when the water table dropped

okay, it stayed all right, and as the ground dried out and rotage, two voids appeared there and there, it got loaded very very intensely in the middle here, and the ground subsided away as well as the material dried out, and the whole thing started to settle. We cannot reverse that, but what we have now done is to drill and group the remaining joints; some of them were closed up, and what's done is done, but we actually drilled down surgically and ejected grout into those slots there and mitigated that for a good period of time. There is still some timber down there has not decayed. It is an ongoing process. But these things really do happen, but provided one does one's investigation, it is possible to mitigate from the grout was it would have been. In this case the only other solution would have been complete underpinning which would have been a most enormous operation, because of the smallness of the rooms and the depths to which we should have to have gone.

So those are my examples, which I hope give you feel for how, as a practising engineer, one encounters timber in funny places in historic buildings, and it is not just the pure timber structure. But I would like to think too, and I would like to suggest a few ideas, and I don't know what the answers to these ones are, that no review of historic timber buildings can be complete without looking at the future historic buildings, and what we are going to do about them? We are designing those at the moment, well some of them. But buildings as young as 25 years are being Listed. What are we going to do about the conservation of them? What is the right way to conserve or repair plywood, particularly if it was not properly detailed? How does one deal; in situ with a factory-made component like a glue laminated timber beam? What about wood wool slabs? Are they going to be manufactured again? Are we going to replace them? I don't know. What do we do about board marked concrete? These are all to me quite fascinating questions, because we don't know quite what we are going to do yet, but what I think comes out of all this is that timber is always there in historic buildings. It is already there in the historic buildings of the future, and I think that the whole issue of timber in historic buildings is absolutely fascinating, and I hope that I have shown you some examples of interest so that you see the broad range of situation where one comes across this very interesting material.

DESIGNING OUT TIMBER DETERIORATION

Dr Jagjit Singh

Introduction

Timber is environmentally friendly material and is natural, non-toxic, organic, recyclable, renewable, and biodegradable. Timber is the oldest material used by mankind in construction and in structural integrity it can be equivalent to pre-stressed concrete lintel, if it is kept dry and well ventilated in buildings. It is easy to use in construction, causes low pollution and requires far less energy to convert into usable products than materials such as steel and concrete therefore less environmental impact.

Timber in historic buildings, abbeys, churches, timber frame buildings, barns, castles, jetties, bridges and other structures is inherently susceptible to fungal and insect infestation and decay, if it is not well designed, kept dry and well ventilated. Once the infestation has started it will continue to propagate, if the conditions are favourable, until eventually the timber member can no longer sustain loads (see photograph 1).

In Great Britain we are the champions of the following facts;

- Misdiagnosis of timber infestation and decay in buildings
- Misunderstanding of timber infestation and decay in buildings
- Mistreatment of timber infestation and decay in buildings

In addition to the above I would like to inform you today that the damage and destruction caused by timber decay organisms is less than the damage and destruction caused by the professionals who treat these infestations.

In my presentation today, I will further corroborate the above three points with some case studies.

Fungal Infestation and Timber Decay

Timber decay in buildings is caused by a variety of insect and fugal decay organisms. The most common fungi to cause damage to building structures are the dry rot fungus (*Serpula lacrymans*), cellar rot fungus (*Coniphora puteana*) and wet rot fungi (*Antrodia vaillantii, Antrodia xantha, Asterostroma* spp, *Donkioporia expansa, Paxillus panuoides, Antrodia xantha, Phellinus contignuus* and *Tyromyces placentus*).

The dry rot fungus, *Serpula lacrymans* (Schumach. ex Fr. Gray), (previously known as *Merulius lacrymans*), is the most important timber decay fungus in buildings in northern and central Europe, and is also of serious concern in Japan and Australia. *Serpula lacrymans* is the most virulent form of fungal attack in building timbers, and buildings of traditional construction are particularly vulnerable to this form of decay.

Not only does the fungus bring about the dramatic decay of timber, but it is also able to spread through a building from one timber location to another across non-nutritional surfaces. The fungus has a serious impact on the housing stock of the United Kingdom and also causes concern when dealing with the conservation of buildings of architectural or historic value.

Characteristics of Decay

Main Characteristics of Timber Decay

There are four key characteristics that can be used in the identification of fungal growths:

mycelium, appearance of decaying wood, strands and fruiting bodies (Sporophores).

The environmental conditions in the building, combined with the quality of timber in construction and use of the building play an important role in the type and characteristics of infestation and decay.

The first sign of decay in the building sometimes is the fruiting bodies of the decay fungi, and this is an indication that the environmental conditions are not suitable for the infestation and decay. This sometimes mainly the results of fixing water leaks and introducing ventilation in the infested areas.

The following notes compare these characteristics for dry rot with those of wet rots.

Main characteristics of fungal decay of timber.

Characteristic	Dry rot	Wet rot
Mycelium	Damp conditions: masses of tears on silky white surface, with bright lemon patches. Drier conditions: thin skin of silver grey in colour, with deep lilac tinges.	High humidity: yellow to brownish in colour
Decayed wood	Deep cuboidal cracking associated with differential drying shrinkage. Reduction in weight. Dull brown in colour. Resinous smell gone	Cuboidal cracking on smaller scale. Thin skin of sound wood. Weight loss. Localised infection
Strands (Rhizomorphs)	3-mm in diameter. Brittle when dry. Off-white/dark grey in colour	Thinner than dry rot. Flexible when dry. Creamy white in colour.
Sporophores (Fruiting bodies)	Tough, fleshy pancake or bracket-shaped, varying from a few centimetres to a metre across. Ridged centre: yellow-ochre when young, darkening to rusty when mature. Lilac/white edged. Distinct mushroom smell.	Not very common in buildings Musty smell, rather than mushroom smell associated with an active growth of dry rot red

Extensive timber decay caused by dry rot (Serpula lacrymans)

Dry Rot (*Serpula lacrymans*)

Dry rot infestation in building is treated as cancer of building. The fungus grows in cavities and voids, where the environmental conditions are conducive to its growth and proliferation. The development of the dry rot will not happen in timber of low moisture content. It is generally considered, though difficult to measure precisely, that moisture levels in wood need to be over 20% (weight for weight) before dry rot can develop. This is not much higher than the moisture level found in well seasoned wood (around 12-16%) but nevertheless it is a level that should not occur in a well maintained building. At low moisture levels water in wood is intimately associated with wood fibres. Above 20% moisture content allows 'free' water starts to appear in the wood structure and it is this free water which is essential for fungal growth and development. The 20% level is termed the 'fibre saturation point'. It is as well to be aware that precise moisture measurements in wood are probably of less importance than changes and trends within buildings. The dry rot fungus has occupied a specialized ecological niche in buildings in Europe with its unique biology, and is only known to occur in the wild in the Himalayas. The author has led several Himalayan expeditions for the search for wild dry rot in the Himalayas with a view to gathering information on its biology, ecology and genetics in the wild.

The ravages of the dry rot fungus are familiar (see picture 2), as is the destruction caused by attempts to eradicate it, particularly involving the use of chemicals.

The vast majority of properties in the United Kingdom contain a significant amount of wood, ranging from structural timbers (such as joists, breassummes, rafters, wall plates, purlins and timber safe lintels) and finishings (such as timber panelling and boarding, skirtings).

Inspection

The correct and early diagnosis of dry rot requires an understanding of the pathology of the fungus as well as a sound knowledge of building construction. Determining the presence of hidden or built-in timbers is crucial to a full and accurate detection of the fungus. There are a number of non-destructive techniques that the surveyor can use to help in arriving at a correct diagnosis. In order to detect the type and extent of fungal decay, remedial measures could entail the loss of decorative finishes, extensive exposures and damage to the fabric of the building: such work can be very expensive.

Dry rot in its early stages is difficult to distinguish from other wood rots without the benefit of laboratory analysis. This involves growing samples of the fungi

Dry rot fruiting bodies to timber staircase, causing extensive structural damage.

on an artificial medium under controlled conditions. Various media based on oatmeal, wheat flour and malt extract can be used as a nutrient to encourage fruiting of the fungus.

In its terminal stages when the fruiting bodies or sporophores have developed brown spore dust dry rot is relatively easy to distinguish from wet rot. The former, however, can spread to other timbers, even through masonry materials, whereas the latter is always restricted to the locus of the moisture source. This ability to spread is one of the distinguishing and menacing feature of S. lacrymans.

Other techniques used included microscopy, laboratory culture and identification of fungi and insects, hot wire anemometry and electronic moisture and RH measurement (see photograph). More exotic techniques may sometimes be useful such as infra-red thermography, short wave radar, automatic weather stations, ultrasonic detection of timber and total building monitoring using specialist data loggers. It is important to remember that any technique must be carefully justified because the value of the information from techniques not routinely used or properly calibrated can be very limited.

Remedial chemical timber treatment can cause damage to the health of building occupants and is a cause for concern to environmental health authorities.

It is the lack of understanding of the biology and ecology of the dry rot fungus that has led to this radical treatment and hence considerable damage to building

Dr Jagjit Singh using hammer probe to measure deep moisture content of timber.

Dry rot mycelium growth to the timber floor, causing extensive structural decay to the floor.

fabric. It is hoped that the fundamental scientific knowledge gained through multi-disciplinary research should enable us to reach a better understanding of the fungus and to develop.safer, more effective, ecological control techniques and strategies. Not only is fungal

infection of timber unsightly and potentially hazardous to human health, it can also adversely affect the structural integrity of the timbers as well as disrupt the use of the building.

The increasing appreciation of unique environmental credentials of wood and the European Government vision 2010 will enable the wider use of timber in construction.

It is therefore important that the building or structure is regularly surveyed, monitored and evaluated for timber decay to prevent failure or collapse, which could result in loss of use or personal injury, The lack of maintenance and knowledge about timber in construction, the environmental factors and the role-play by timber decay fungi and insects causing a range of failures to the timber used in construction. The following pictures illustrate the typical failures of timber in construction (see picture 4 and 5).

Based on this information, environmental control measures can be put in place to prevent further advancement of the decay.

The Conservation Approach

The conservation approach involves carrying out regular inspections using a range of non-destructive investigation techniques. This approach enables a specific maintenance programme to be drawn up and ensures that the loss of historic fabric is kept to a minimum.

A number of other in-situ methods for timber decay assessment are available; however, these involve destructive techniques and have had varying degrees of success in detecting decay and predicting the residual strength of timber members. The analysis of decay organisms with destructive sampling is neither sympathetic nor acceptable to the conservation of historic churches, castles, abbeys, monuments and other landmarks. Furthermore, remedial chemical treatments for woodworm, death-watch beetles, dry rot and wet rots are very expensive and often cause more damage to the health of building fabric and people than the infestation itself.

The majority of environmental problems are associated with building defects leading to water ingress, condensation and dampness in the building fabric. Severe salt efflorescence, staining, blistering of finishes and timber decay in buildings are mainly the result of water penetration.

The causes of deterioration are influenced by the internal building environment, which has a varied microclimate depending upon the building structure and the envelope of the internal building fabric.

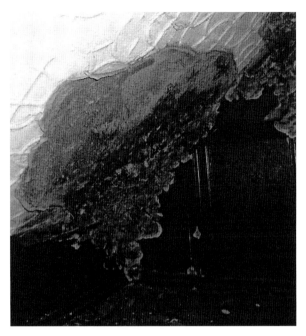

Dry rot fruiting body to the under stair void causing structural damage to the staircase and wall panelling

Site Investigation and Resistograph Methodology

The Resistograph drill does require a little time to penetrate into and back out of the timber member. Care must be taken to ensure the Resistograph is held steady while drilling, otherwise damage to the bit will occur. Care must also be taken to avoid any metallic obstructions that may be in the path of the drill bit.

Large numbers of timber members can be inspected in relatively short periods of time using the Resistograph. This is advantageous since the longevity and cost-effective maintenance of historic timber structures relies on early detection of decay and preservation of the members.

This methodology involves the use of a Resistograph drill which drives a 3mm diameter drill bit up to 440mm into the timber member. As the bit penetrates the wood the rotational resistance is shown on an LED display and recorded on a print-out chart. This gives an immediate profile and permanent record of the internal condition of the timber.

Regions of sound wood are shown as high resistance to forward motion of the bit. As the bit enters a decayed region, the resistance to forward motion is reduced and a low signal level is recorded.

Environmental Monitoring

To determine the causes of the above, environmental monitoring and investigation is best carried out. This is done by employing a range of hand held instrumentation, physical sampling and sensor technology to monitor various parameters within the fabric of the building.

The first step to investigation of a problem building is to carry out a thorough inspection of the building for defects. The second step is:

• to establish moisture contents in affected materials, such as timber, plaster, masonry, insulation materials and textiles.

• to establish the humidity, temperature and dew point in the environment. Both internally and externally.

• to investigate in greater detail as necessary the moisture profiles in large dimension timbers and across masonry masses.

This information can be determined by:

• moisture contents of timber can be taken directly by the use of resistance based moisture meters. Probes can also be used to measure moisture contents at depth in large section timbers and those built into masonry.

• surface moisture readings in plaster and masonry can be taken using moisture meters. These will indicate if a wall is dry but can give false readings of dampness, see below.

• where possible mortar samples should be taken of the areas affected to determine accurately the moisture and salt content of the masonry. This does however have the disadvantage of not being non-destructive.

• data loggers can be used to measure the environmental parameters, temperature, Humidity and dew point both internally and externally.

• specialist probes can be used to measure moisture across masonry walls.

The results of all or some of the above tests will establish the cause and enable a solution to the problem to be put forward.

Environmental Data Loggers

Data loggers measuring temperature and humidity are useful to determine whether there is for instance an abnormally high humidity or risk of condensation in a building. If readings are taken on both the interiors and exteriors of the building dew points within materials such as masonry masses can be calculated.

Stabilising the Historic Environment

Once the above investigations have been carried out a strategy can be put forward to stabilise the building environment.

It is important to stabilise the historic building environment. For the holistic and sustainable conservation and preservation of the building, various building works will be required to prevent further water penetration and to maximise ventilation to damp affected materials.

Correction of these building defects, combined with measures to dry down the wet areas and to protect the decorative interior finishes by allowing ventilation of the wet areas, will prevent further deterioration.

Until the drying out of the building fabric and its associated timber elements is completed, any other actions to remedy the deterioration problems will be ineffective and a waste of time and resources. Continuous long-term monitoring and preventative maintenance of the building may be necessary and will provide the following information:

- on the state of moisture equilibrium and balance (moisture sources, reservoirs and sinks) in the building environment, building fabric and structural elements as the building dries out;

- will allow co-ordination and scheduling of work stages to prioritise the remedial work to achieve acceptable levels of moisture in the masonry and timber to prevent future deterioration problems;

- will allow a cost-effective, long-term holistic approach to environmental stabilisation of the historic environment.

Further Reading

Singh J: Building Mycology, Management of Health and Decay in Buildings, London, Spon, 1994.

Singh J: Dry rot and other wood-destroying fungi: their occurrence, biology, pathology and control. Indoor + Built Environment 1999; 8: 3-20.

Singh J, White N: Timber decay in buildings - research, remedies and reform: in Proc of Reconstruction and Conservation of Historical Wood Symposium, TU Zvolen, 1995.

Singh J, Beth-Andersen J, Elborne, SA, Singh S, Walker B, Goldie, F: The search for wild dry rot fungus (*Serpula lacrymans*) in the Himalayas. The Mycologist 1993:7(3);124-130.

Singh J and Aneja K R 1999 *From Ethnomycology to fungal biotechnology, Exploiting fungi from natural resources for novel products*, published by Kluwer Academic/Plenum Publishers

Singh J and Walker W 1996 *Allergy problems in Buildings*, Mark Allen Publishing Ltd.

Singh J, and White N 1995 *Environmental preservation of timber in buildings*, Published by Oscar Faber, St Albans UK.

GOOD MANAGEMENT: AVOIDING DRY ROT DECAY

John Palfreyman, University of Abertay, Dundee

Like the last speaker, I feel slightly guilty about giving a paper on one of the problems to do with timber, and again, I am going to talk about dry rot. But the message I want to get over is that it is not the timber's fault. The reason why we get dry rot in buildings is due to bad maintenance, bad design or inappropriate use, and as we have seen from some of the slides this morning, and the ones that I will show as well, timber can last a long, long period of time in the built environment, if it is looked after properly.

Now for the past 4 years, my group at the University of Abertay Dundee has been working in partnership with Historic Scotland on a project to look at the parameters associated with the environmental control of dry rot. In particular, we are interested in looking at managing dry rot out of the system without relying on the type of chemical treatments that are normally used. The fruits of the work of the research group have been published today in a Technical Advice Note which is designed for practitioners who face the problems of dry rot in buildings they look after, and the Technical Advice Note is supported by a great deal of scientific data which is present in the research report, which is also being published today.

To introduce the nature of the presentation: I will to say a little about dry rot, and the organism that causes dry rot, Serpula lacrymans. I am going to say something about some of the research that has been undertaken for Historic Scotland, so a bit of a change of gear here. There will be some science, I am afraid. I am going to talk about dry rot in historic buildings; I am going to say a little about the TAN we have produced and some messages for the building manager.

Now the problem, that many of you will be familiar with, is that dry rot can totally devastate a building and we have seen some wonderful examples from Dr Singh in the previous paper. Decay by S.lacrymans the dry rot fungus, is not self-limiting like decay by many other organisms which cause timber degradation. In other words, it does not just go so far and stop. It just keeps going, and this is the fascinating problem for a scientist. Companies have traded on the fears of the organism to rush customers into expensive treatment regimes, and I always think has stopped. Then I come across an example showing that it has not stopped, and just last week I was called in to look at a floor in a village hall in Newtyle, just outside Dundee. Within 18 months of making alterations to this building someone had gone through the wooden floor of the hall and the companies were telling the owners they had to get something done immediately, or the thing would get far, far worse. And in fact there were very simple things that could be done.

We have got to a situation where building owners tend to think that decay caused by dry rot is inevitable. In addition treatment of dry rot concentrates on the

Clearing, cleaning and maintaining the guttering in a building is essential

immediate problem and tends to be less concerned about the causes of the problem. From a personal point of view, I was told a few years ago that there was no point in researching dry rot, as it can be eradicated by removing decayed timber, replacing with treated timber, and irrigating walls etc. In other words 'there is not really a problem' but we all know there is.

In fact, the dry rot fungus is very sensitive to its environment, it is very easily inactivated by drying. Timber decay is not inevitable. Repairs do not have to be immediate. *S.lacrymans* is an interesting organism and is worth further study in its own right, in my view. So the sorts of questions we were asking in our research centred around the question 'do the timber parts of buildings necessarily decay?' If not, what are the most important factors in ensuring survival? It is now apparent that these factors include maintenance, inspection, good design, avoiding potential moisture problems and above all, in my view, a knowledge and understanding of what is going on within a building. So just to have a few historic building slides; here is a church in Telc (Czech Republic) that I visited with Dr Singh and Ingval Maxwell, from Historic Scotland a few years ago. The timbers are a few hundred years old and they have survived very well. Here is a curling club hut near where I live in Forfar, which is pretty old, and has survived with minimal maintenance for at least 50 years, possibly longer; and one of my favourite wooden structures – a Norwegian 'stave kirke' – I showed this slide a few years ago, and someone informed me that the building had been burnt down a

couple of years ago, unfortunately, but it wasn't attacked by dry rot, it was attacked by political insurgents, unfortunately.

So why do we get dry rot, well if you look at the state of some buildings it is hardly surprising. Problems all over the place with bad drain water systems, defects in roofs, leaking internal plumbing and even sometimes in new situations – the slide shows a new oak beam that has been put into a damp wall. And people will say that you do not get any signs of dry rot you just 'fall through a floor' or part of a staircase collapses. In my view the causes of dry rot are normally very obvious and I challenge anyone to find dry rot when there were no external signs, although we still believe that it happens behind walls, and there is no knowledge of what is going on. But you have to look carefully. And we know the sort of things that the dry rot fungus can do: this is a church in Glasgow that Neil Ross from Historic Scotland took me round a year or two ago, which made the hairs on the back of my neck stand up when we saw what was going on. This is a building in Dundee, a Victorian building, which was divided into 4 flats, and upstairs and downstairs spent 10 years arguing about whose fault the dry rot was, until somebody went through the floors, and that stopped the arguments.

So dry rot is still a serious problem. However not that many people do research on it, and at Abertay we have developed a research group that is looking at a range of aspects of dry rot and the fungus that causes it,

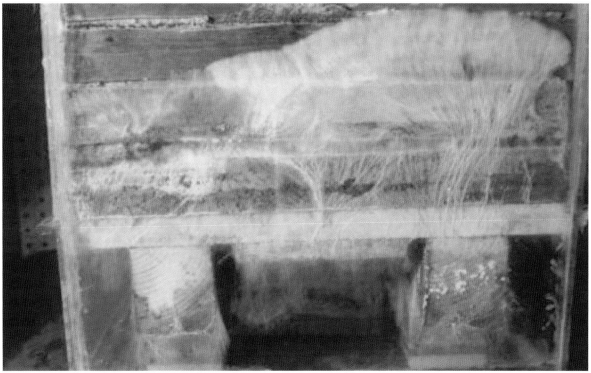

Small models showed that moisture was the crucialm element in establishing environmental control

S.lacrymans; for example, Environmental Control, which is what I am going to talk about mainly today. We are also interested to find out why the fungus decides to grow on one part of a building, and not another part of the building. We are investigating the origins of the organism and have undertaken genetic analysis on material that Dr Singh found in the Himalayas. We are interested in the physiology of the organism and whether or not it can cause stone decay. We have worked on this with Maureen Young from the Robert Gordon University who is also funded by Historic Scotland.

Looking first at environmental control, the causative organism of dry rot *S.lacrymans* is like any other organism, it is sensitive to its environment. The built environment is not necessarily a suitable environment in which the organism can flourish. Non-wooden material in buildings can influence the process. Dry rot is quite rare in buildings which are purely made of timber. It is the mixture of timber and masonry which causes the problem. The reasons why dry rot occurs in the built environment are related to moisture and high humidity, and the conditions allowing the development of dry rot normally occur because of bad management, or inappropriate design or use. A few years ago, there were a number of companies in the UK starting to suggest the idea of environmental control, and Historic Scotland were interested in setting up a scientific study to actually look at the validity of environmental control. So we have looked at environmental sensitivity. Is it correct that the dry rot fungus sensitive

to its environment (it would be very unusual if it was not), and what are the limits of this sensitivity? Can the fungus become resistant to environmental change, either in the long or short term? What are the important parameters? We were also interested in non-wood materials in buildings: can they influence the decay process, some types of buildings seem particularly susceptible to dry rot. For example, compare wooden buildings which tend not to get dry rot, with mixed construction buildings which do get dry rot. The introduction of new materials into buildings can result in problems. (There was a well known case in Scandinavia when house holders started putting rock wool insulation in timber buildings, which had never suffered from dry rot; as soon as the rock wool went in, cases of dry rot started to appear.) And can the dry rot fungus degrade non-woody materials?

The environmental control research we initiated started at a small scale using what scientists call microcosms. Essentially experiments in sandwich boxes, but microcosm sounds more scientific. We then moved on to small scale models to look at environmental control and finally, a couple of years ago, we built some large-scale models of bits of buildings to investigate whether you could use environmental control in these. And just briefly, I will also say something about the stone studies that we have done.

Microcosm experiments: fungi were grown on a petri dish within a sandwich box. These experiments were designed to look at the effects of air flow on the growth

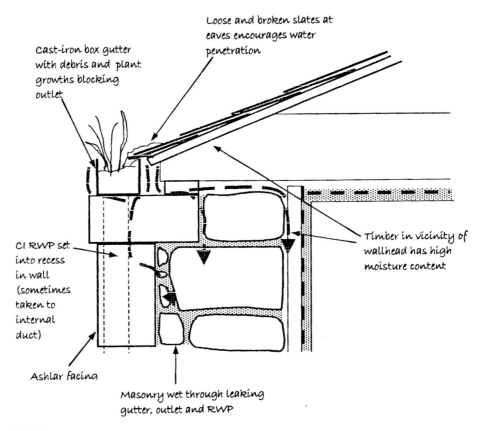

Loose and broken slates at eaves encourages water penetration

Cast-iron box gutter with debris and plant growths blocking outlet

CI RWP set into recess in wall (sometimes taken to internal duct)

Timber in vicinity of wallhead has high moisture content

Ashlar facing

Masonry wet through leaking gutter, outlet and RWP

Detail of a box gutter set

of the dry rot fungus. Another type of microcosm experiment looked at the growth of the fungus on wood, which was in contact with either masonry, or a variety of other materials in the form of tiles. And the salient findings from this research were that airflow normally inhibits fungal growth completely. However, if you had a very low air flow, and this is much lower than you would expect, say, in your sub floor space, you could stimulate growth, and the fungus tried to grow away from the air flow. Next thing we found was wood/masonry combinations promoted decay. If you tried to decay timber when it was in contact with plastic tiles, which are relatively inert, then the timber did not decay. And we looked at different types of sandstone, we found that sandstones with a range of very different mineral composition all supported decay. From the scientific point of view, one of the most interesting things we found was that sandstone, which is rich in iron, resulted in elevate iron levels at the fungal growth front. This means that the fungus can transport iron from masonry into timber, and one of the things that stops organism from decaying timber is often lack of iron – because iron is used in the enzyme processes that decay timber. This ability to transport iron may well be the key to why *S.lacrymans* is so effective, because it can take iron out of masonry, put it into timber, and then use the iron to help in the degradation of the timber.

So these were the results of our microcosm experiments. We then started building small-scale models – and I should mention my colleague, Gordon Low, who did this work. Small models showed that control of moisture was the crucial element in establishing environmental control. We would get *S.lacrymans* growing in small models which consisted of a mixture of bricks and timber – if you took the water out of the system, then the organism stopped growing. If you put aeration into the system, then the organism stops growing. Put water back into system and seal it back up again, i.e. prevent aeration, and *S.lacrymans* started to regrow.

Then our research moved to full-scale models of parts of Scottish buildings. The first model was a wall-floored joint and was one of the three models designed to demonstrate the use of environmental control. The model was wired up so we could follow moisture levels within the construction. The model was infected with *S.lacrymans*, and then it was treated just through airflow. No chemicals, just airflow and by putting an airflow into the model, you could stop the growth of the dry rot fungus. Model two represented a roof structure. We were not sure whether these models would work because no one had built anything like this before, but it did not take long before the models were absolutely full of the dry rot fungus. We also demonstrated that the fungus could communicate within itself over quite long distances. Early on in the experiment we started to produce a fruit body in one corner of one of the models. Later the fungus found an escape from the model and started producing a fruit body outside the model. As soon as that happened, the internal fruit body started to decompose. So the fungus was talking to itself over a distance of about a metre and a half.

Conclusions from these models were that the growth of *S.lacrymans* is, as we thought, very sensitive to available moisture; increasing airflow and moving water sources stopped growth – at least on the macro scale. In the short term I am sure that the organism survives, but it doesn't grow and it does not decay timber. If favourable conditions return then the fungus will revive and start to decompose timber elements once again. So in these big models, if we open them up everything would stop. Closing them up again, and the fungus started growing, but if you opened them up and got rid of the moisture, then the organism stopped growing. There were no problems with contaminating organisms. My microbiological colleagues said these models would not work, because we would get too many other fungi growing in them, but the only thing that grows in abundance is the dry rot fungus. Finally, communication within the fungal biomass was possible over what were relatively long distances.

Now to briefly look at the work we did with the Robert Gordon University. In the slide it is possible to see very fine fibres (hyphae) of *S.lacrymans* growing on stone, and the fibres get covered with crystals of calcium oxalate. (All our slides of fungi on stone were taken in conjunction with Maureen Young at RGU). These experiments showed that *S.lacrymans* developed in conjunction with the crystals of calcium oxalate; iron could be transported to the growth front as I mentioned before. There is no evidence of overt stone decay, which was good from the point of view of the conservationist by disappointing to us scientists. The degradation caused on stone by *S.lacrymans* is only minor. Traditionally it is thought the calcium oxalate that accumulates around the fungal hyphae is produced to inhibit the inhibitory effects of oxalic acid which the organism produces. However I think the oxalic acid is produced to inhibit the effects of calcium, but that is another story.

What does this mean to the building manager? Well, dry rot is not an inevitable occurrence in buildings. Elevated timber moisture levels cause the dry rot. Timber moisture levels can increase due to bad design, bad maintenance or inappropriate change of use. To prevent dry rot from occurring, it is important to understand potential moisture sources in buildings. This requires an understanding of the construction of the building, and some of the common problems that

are found within historic buildings, are illustrated in the following slide – and I am just going to flip through these, because they are all taken from the Technical Advice Note drawn by Denis Urquhart – for example here is the route of moisture movement in the windowhead detail. Here is the problem that can result from interstitial condensation on flat roofs which are covered with metal. Here is water penetration around a box gutter step. These diagrams, and others, are present in the Technical Advice Note, and will give guidance on how to look for how moisture may have penetrated into your buildings.

What are the conditions for the growth of *S.lacrymans*? There are lots of things that are required, but actually the most important thing is a source of water source. To get decay wood with high levels of moisture, or relatively high levels of moisture is required. Masonry with moisture in it accelerates growth of *S.lacrymans*. High humidity – if the humidity in a building is reduced, then the fungus stops growing. Air movement: stagnant air combined with moisture will result in dry rot. If you have ineffective building management, you are likely to get dry rot. There is more about analysis of how moisture levels are increased in buildings within the TAN. Perhaps the most important reason why we get dry rot in the built environment is lack of knowledge. If you understand how a building works, and you understand what causes dry rot, then you will not get dry rot in your buildings.

Dr Singh mentioned the case of dry rot in Keith Hall, just outside Aberdeen, and Keith Hall is actually a case study within the Technical Advice Note. The TAN contains a three dimensional diagram which relates the moisture sources that were found in Keith Hall, to all the areas of fungal decay, and of course the two things superimpose on each other. Where there was moisture, fungal decay has resulted. There is information, also, in the TAN on some of the other wood decay fungi that are found in buildings; top of the list is *S.lacrymans*, top of the list, because it is the organism that does the most damage. There are a number of other organisms which tend not to be so aggressive, because they do not have some of the facilities that *S.lacrymans* has. It is important to have good identification as was said in the previous talk.

The essential stages of treating dry rot by environmental control area as follows; first of all the production of a comprehensive report, including information on both timber condition and moisture sources. Next, the development of a holistic strategy for alleviating the problem. Then comes the works, and then the development of a long term maintenance strategy, to prevent reoccurrence. Details of this process are again given in the Technical Advice Note. Monitoring is the key to prevent reoccurrence, otherwise it just happens again. Other aspects of environmental control which are discussed in the Advice Note: first of all mothballing. We sometimes see situations where people cannot afford to do anything about a dry rot outbreak in a building and they just leave it. And the building slowly gets worse and worse. Owners will say they cannot do anything, because they cannot afford to, however often there are many things that can be done which do not actually cost very much. So mothballing is an alternative when funds are restricted. Another issue is preventing a decay situation from deteriorating. So, for example, correcting defects in rainwater system, other building defects – increasing underfloor ventilation, removing wall coverings, exposing internal downpipes, stripping off plaster from safe lintels etc; these are all things which will slow down the decay process significantly if it is not possible to do a full repair. So environmental control essentially means manipulating building conditions to produce an environment which is not conducive to the growth of the dry rot fungus. In its purest form, this environment could be produced purely by physical means. This may not always be possible, so control systems of different 'purity' may need to be considered.

For example, the policy related to a specific situation might be that there is to be no replacement of any timber, retention of all original materials and no chemical treatments. Alternatively it might be necessary to use minimal replacement of timber, strengthening of decayed timber, and perhaps some minimal use of preservatives. The normal method of treating dry rot, however, is replacing infected and suspect timbers with new, and possibly preserved treated timbers, and more widespread use of preservatives and we really do not feel this is justified on the basis of the work that we have done. There is this information on this in the TAN, but the important message is maintenance, monitoring; dry rot will return if appropriate conditions develop. There can be no long-term guarantee that dry rot will not occur, but regular inspection can reduce risk. Remote monitoring systems can help, and further information is present in the TAN. Most important is to overcome is the concern that is illustrated in a book that was published in the early 1990s called, "Dry Rot the Beast in the Basement" – there is 'some dreadful thing existing out there which can decompose our buildings'. Yes it can, but what we need to do is to change perceptions, and there is a lot of information there which can help.

Finally, I would like to acknowledge the fact that the research at the University of Abertay in Dundee has been supported by a large number of people and organisations. Particular people I would like to thank are Denis Urquhart, who joined me in the latter stages of producing the Technical Advice Note, to make sure that there was plenty of information in there for practitioners, my colleague Dr Nia White who helped with the project design, former student Dr Gordon Low who did much of the research that I am reporting on, and Historic Scotland who funded our research over a period of years. I would also like to thank the various practitioners who have helped our group over the years.

PREVENTING INSECT ATTACK

Brian Ridout, Ridout Associates

The use of complex formulations to control insects in buildings, proliferated in the 1950s, and by the time we come to the 1960s, we have developed an industry, a remedial industry, which consists of 2 men and a van coming out with a spray lance and a lot of chemicals, and treating everything in your building. By the time we get to the 1990s, the concept has changed somewhat, and people are really beginning to think they don't want so many chemicals in their buildings.

John has talked to you about environmental control. There is this apparently new idea, environmental control of decay organisms. It isn't a new idea at all; it is the chemical treatments that are the new idea. The first book on environmental control of dry rot actually appeared in 1797, so that is a very, very old idea. It is a 20th-century concept that we need to fling a lot of chemicals at timbers in our buildings. If we are going to try and get away from chemicals, then we have to understand the natural habitats of the creatures we are dealing with, and we have to understand what they do in their own home, as it were, because none of these things, none of these organisms are particularly adapted to attack timber in buildings. It is simply that if we keep the conditions in our building in a way that mirror the organisms natural requirements, then that organism will decay.

So we have looked at the fungus, and now I am just going to have a look at wood-boring insects, using the same kind of logic that Jagjit used earlier on, to discuss fungi.

So, what does a wood-boring insect do when it is at home? Well their natural role is to attack dead parts of trees, fallen logs and take these things back into the natural carbon cycle, and they vary somewhat in the way that they do this, and in their environmental requirements. If we have a log on the forest floor, then we will get a range of beetles which will invade it, and they make in turn, things like weevils. Weevils are insects we find in our buildings quite often. You have got two there; a big one and a small one. The small one is the lesser of two weevils. I can't resist that one. But the point about these is that weevils are living in an environment where there is plenty of water, and there is plenty of fungus. Their natural habitat is to attack timbers when they are very wet, and therefore in our buildings that is what they will do, and just a picture again, just to show the kind of conditions which might

also promote weevil attack. Clearly, if you get rid of the moisture, you will get rid of the weevils. In fact weevils are very, very sensitive to moisture loss, and are fairly easily lost by just changing the conditions.

There are however a whole bunch of beetles whose natural habitat is a dead branch on standing trees, and these are, at least as far as the ones that concern us, the beetles which would include the furniture beetle, death watch beetle, and numerous other ones throughout the world. Now the thing about a dead branch on a standing tree is that it is wet for a long period of time. It is also dry sometimes. Now these things are somewhat tolerant of dry conditions, which gives them quite a good advantage when attacking timber in buildings. The beetle does not feed. It is the lava that feeds, and the lava is sensitive to moisture. Even though, they can tolerate dry conditions, if you keep the moisture content of your timber in your building down below 12-15%, something like that, throughout the year, then you will deplete the beetle population. If you get it down below that 10%, you will kill them quite quickly. The reason we deplete the population is that the dryer the timber, the longer it takes for the lava to reach full size. The longer it takes the lava to reach full size, the smaller the adult beetle that is produced. Small beetles produce fewer eggs. So the whole population goes into a spiral of decline.

The other thing about a dead branch on a standing tree is that it will never be free from decay, there will always be some fungus in there, and that is quite important to some, indeed to most, of the beetles. They can readily attack the outer sap? of the timber, but they cannot attack the hardwood – at least a durable species like Scots Pine or Oak – they cannot attack the hard wood, unless the chemistry of that hard wood has been modified by a fungus. It does not require much fungus, and the fungus does not even have to be alive when the beetles attack, but the hard wood chemistry has to be modified before these beetles can damage the timber. But the sapwood bit is for us very important.

You see here this is actually Death Watch beetle damage. The top part there, the light timber is the sapwood; the dark timber is the hardwood, and the beetles haven't managed to attack the hardwood at all. So if we bear that in mind, then we can start to analyse what we see. I am hopeless at technology. What we see here is a post, in fact from Salisbury Cathedral – lots and lots of these posts in Salisbury Cathedral. The interesting thing is that they have beetle holes on one side here, and the side round the corner. No beetle holes on one side there, and the holes round the corner. Very interesting distribution of beetle damage to the timber. A remedial bod came along and he said, "The beetle attacks wood. This Cathedral is made of wood. There is a lot of timber there that hasn't been attacked yet, and therefore the beetle is active and we have to treat the entire roof." If you accept that policy, then obviously that is what you do, but if you think what's happening, and you remember these are fundamentally pests of sapwood, then you can actually see what in fact you have got.

We had a log. We sawed the log through the sapwood, on the top, then we sawed the log into 4 through the hard wood, so we end up with 2 sides with a bit of sap wood attached to them, and 2 sides with the pure hard wood; that is why we have got beetle holes on two sides, and not on the other two sides. Just the way in which the timber has been converted. Does the timber need treating? Of course, it doesn't. The damage there probably occurred 800 or 900 years ago, and of course the beetle holes doesn't just go because the beetle goes.

Unfortunately if you don't understand the problem, then you can do silly things. This is a church in southern Holland you see the joinery injectors all over it, all over the oak, sapwood damage, and because they did not understand what they were looking at, they have made an awful mess of the roof, and it is entirely unnecessary.

Now the timber we used to use, certainly south of the Border, throughout the 18th and 19th century – softwood timber, Scots Pine came from the forests of northern Europe mainly, and came from old trees – typically 200 or 300 years old. This is in fact a 500 year old Scots Pine tree, photographed the other week in north west Russia, but it is the kind of thing we would have taken our timber from, and when you look at that kind of timber – and this again is a section of work they are doing on a church in Russia – you can see very, very tight grain. This is the sapwood layer. Not much sapwood, it is growing inner wood. There is not much room for it to grow. Most of this is good mature hard wood. By the time we square that up, we have lost most of the sapwood; just a little bit on the corner, and this is all very very high quality timber. There is one other little bit here which is of interest, and that is at the centre, because for the 15 years or so we had juvenile growth in the middle there. Juvenile growth. We know a lot about the properties of juvenile wood as far as papermaking and the like is concerned.

About durability, we know rather less. The information that is available suggests that in many cases until the hard wood production is really under way, juvenile wood is probably not particularly durable. So if we look at a piece of modern redwood from a tree that was about 35 years old when felled, we find all of this is sapwood; no durability. If we take our 15 years growth of juvenile wood we come out to about there, and the only mature hard wood here, which is the wood we want which gives durability, there is a little bit of this sewn here. The problem is that we are not growing our trees for long enough for them to get enough mature hard wood to give us the durability we would have had traditionally.

So the moral of the story, as you say up here, is conserve as much as possible of your historic timber – not just because it is old – but because it has a very good durability.

However, this is modern timber. You can see all the sapwood here. Blue stone fungus. You can see that some of these pieces are mostly sapwood. That timber won't last 5 minutes in buildings unless you put some chemical in it. If we don't want to put chemicals into things, then we have to use the kind of timber that we would have used historically. It is still available, at least in fairly small pieces. This is grade unsorted, Scandinavian grade unsorted timber, joinery quality, and if you look at some of the pieces you can select out nice tight grain; some of these pieces up here would be good; you can miss the pieces with the sap, but you cannot actually select timber as a quality you want to replicate original softwood in historic buildings.

So we can select the timber for our repairs; we can conserve as much as we can of the old timber. We can make sure there is active infestation before we do any treatment. We can get rid of all the junk. Get rid of all the foci and festation you might have there. Chuck it out. If it is falling apart, take it out and burn it. Don't keep rubbish, because the rubbish will support insect pests. Most of these beetles, in fact all of the beetles to my knowledge, fly. They fly prettily readily, even the Death Watch beetle which has been controversial for some years, will fly quite cheerfully if the air temperature exceeds about 17°C, so what about light traps? Typical light trap. UV light trap here. Of the Death Watch beetles – 270 beetles – and I have dissected them all, and they are a bit crisp. But they are all females full of eggs. So your light trap can deplete beetle populations. Having said that, do be careful what sort of light trap you use, because you can get a bat between these bars, they are too far apart.

We have developed something called a "beetle screen" with the Bath Conservation Trust. If anybody is interested in these things, I can give you some details of that. Make sure, if you are going to use light traps that they are bat-friendly, because bats will be attracted to the light and any insects flying around them, and the day you crisp your first bat is probably the last time you use the trap. This is data from Museum in Germany where they have got lots of these traps, testing them. They are not working particularly effectively there because they have got too much incidental light in the building. They are actually in big open buildings. They are very useful for depleting the population. Very useful for monitoring to see whether there is actually any insect activity.

Finally, what about our natural predators? Don't go around trying to destroy the kinds of things that are trying to help you. Spiders are a very good natural predator. They are probably the most important natural predator of the beetles. If you spray a roof, you probably won't make much difference to Death Watch beetle for example, but you will kill off all the spiders that are wandering around looking for them. These things are not particularly there to eat beetles, they are just opportunist predators. But a spider will polish off 20 or 30 beetles during the emergencies. And you could have a surprising number of spiders in your roof. If there are lots and lots and lots of beetles emerging, then the spiders really won't make much difference. But, if you have got a building that is dry, so that your beetle populations are fragmenting into little colonies where things are a bit damper, then the spiders might make a significant difference, and might just be the thing that pushes the beetle population towards extinction.

Remember that you see an awful lot of buildings where you see insect damage, and where the insects have actually died out. It doesn't mean to say that just because you have got furniture beetles in your building that they would always be there. If conditions are changed, then you may be able to get rid of the beetles simply by environmental control. So, don't do anything that harms spiders. Think very very carefully before you start to apply chemicals. Only use chemical treatments if there is a demonstrable need; if there is insect activity; if you can get to the timber that does have that insect activity in it, and then target the treatment, there may be some use for chemicals. But generally speaking, if the timber is older than sort of 20th century, you probably don't have to do anything to get rid of furniture beetle damage, and you might not be able to do anything to get rid of Death Watch beetle damage.

STIRLING CASTLE GREAT HALL,
THE LATER STAGES OF THE RESTORATION

Peter Buchanan, Principal Architect for Historic Scotland

Stirling Castle Axonometric.

In 1991 Historic Scotland set up a team to undertake The Stirling Castle Project and a Project Plan was conceived to enhance the Castle as a visitor attraction, while continuing to conserve it as a monument of international importance.

Before 1990 the buildings were largely unfurnished and visitor interpretation was limited to a few information boards. Proposals were drawn up by the in-house team, for presentation to the Historic Scotland Management Board, the broad outline of the proposals were accepted and an investment appraisal justified the proposed £20 million pounds budget.

South & East Elevation 1960s.

The completion of the Great Hall Restoration was a key element in this plan. The intention being to accelerate the works in order to have the Great Hall restored in time for the new millennium and the 500th anniversary of its construction. The basis for all work was to ensure that the principles and procedures of conservative repair were followed, and only appropriate high quality materials and craftsmanship used. Essential elements of restoration were derived from surviving physical evidence, supported by reference to primary documentary sources and buildings of similar construction and period.

East Elevation 1995.

Interior 1970s.

Interior 1995.

By the middle of the 1990s all the major downtaking, recording, repair and conservation work to the surviving medieval masonry had been completed up to the wallhead level and initial designs were being worked up for the next phase, the reconstruction of the hammerbeam roof.

One of the available sources of information for the Great Hall is a series of etchings, engravings and paintings of the castle from various vantagepoints at different periods. All the drawings show different details, variations in chimney heights, crenellation details, cap houses and ridge ornament. A large quantity of artistic licence was obviously used and the artistic interpretations could not be relied upon for detailed restoration work.

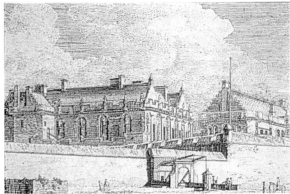

Stirling Castle from the South, Engraving 1753.

Stirling Castle from the Northeast, Slezer 1693.

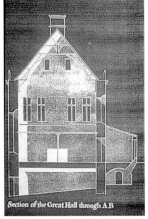

Stirling Castle Great Hall, Board of Ordinance Section, 1719.

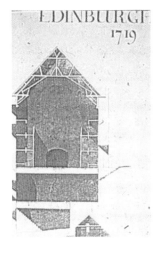

Edinburgh Castle Great Hall, Board of Ordinance Section, 1719.

A further source of information was the detailed survey drawings from the Board of Ordinance of 1719. The drawing of the Great Hall at Stirling, is the only surviving indication of what the hammer beam roof might have looked like. It shows a section through the hall and a principal roof truss. The design for the replacement hammerbeam roof was derived from this drawing and a study of the roof of the Great Hall at Edinburgh Castle.

Edinburgh Castle Great Hall, Interior 1995.

Edinburgh Castle Great Hall, Hammerbeam Detail.

The Great Hall at Edinburgh was built for James IV at about the same time as the Great Hall at Stirling. It is smaller, with a shorter roof span and lower pitch but it would have been constructed by the same craftsmanship using the same traditional construction techniques. We were able to compare the 1719 Board of Ordinance drawing for the Edinburgh roof with our own detailed survey drawings. The Edinburgh hammerbeam is heavily restored and covered in a Victorian decorative scheme, but enough of the original survives for us to be able to compare it with the 1719 drawing. We found the drawing to be accurate and took a leap of faith to assume that the Stirling drawing of the roof structure could also be a close representation of the original.

Original Corbel Stone.

New Corbel Stone.

Model, Internal view, 1:50 scale.

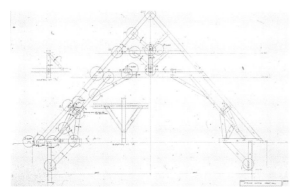

Principal Truss, Working Drawing.

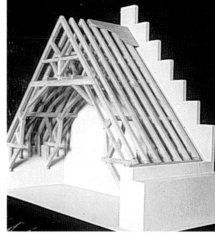

Hammerbeam Roof, Structural Model, 1:20 Scale.

Hammerbeam Roof, Full Size Test Joints.

Our designs for the replacement roof took the main disposition of structural members from the Stirling drawing with all jointing details derived from the Edinburgh roof. Setting out was determined by the stubs of clured off corbels below wall head level in the Hall, each one locating the original position of a principal truss. Design proposals, working drawings and models were produced to detail the beam layouts and jointing systems.

Engineers were consulted to prove the structural stability of the design. With the information available this could only be done in one dimension using estimates as to how the oak pegs would perform. The hammerbeam roof at Edinburgh Castle had been around for five hundred years (although heavily restored) but the engineers were not satisfied that it could be used for a direct structural comparison.

In order to obtain a proper design calculation we constructed full-scale joints and tested them to destruction. The test results enabled us to prove the roof was structurally sound and to allow TRADA to undertake full three dimensional calculations to see how the structure transferred load to the gables and wall heads.

One of the problems raised by the calculations was the amount of lateral thrust imposed by the roof on the wall heads. We already knew this was a problem as the West wall of the hall is out of alignment by about a 450mm at the wall head. The East wall is buttressed by a stair tower, which acted to contained the forces. The west wall had no buttress and its paired windows and large chimney flues meant the upper level masonry did not have sufficient mass to restrain the outward forces. As we were intending to put back a similar roof to the one that had caused the wall to fail, we had to provide a solution to counteract the forces. We simply resolved the forces by placing tie bars between wall head beams. These are being monitored by strain gauges and can be removed if the loading on the wall head proves to be insubstantial.

Our calculations indicated a requirement for just under 100 cubic metres of sawn oak or approx. 350 trees. Forest Enterprise was approached at the end of 1993 to see if they could supply the required quality and quantity of Scottish oak. Following a period of negotiation with Scottish Natural Heritage, agreement was reached to extract oak from designated Sites of Special Scientific Interest (SSSIs) near Strathyre and Aberfoyle. These oak forests were originally planted as a cash crop, grown and coppiced for the tannin in the bark which was used in the tanning industry up until the 1930s. These trees were ideal for our use being straight tall and of small diameter. By selectively felling and deer fencing throughout the woods we allowed regeneration of the forest. As no mechanical

Strathyre Oak Forest, Tree Felling.   *Strathyre Oak Forest, Log Extraction.*

equipment was allowed in the SSSIs the trees were taken to the roadside by shire horse to minimise the disturbance to the forest floor.

The selected logs were uplifted from the roadside and taken to a sawmill for conversion into beams. All the beams in the roof structure have a boxed heart section. This means that the four sides are cut from the log leaving the heart of the tree running through the centre of the beam. The boxed heart creates a strong beam that is less likely to twist or warp as they dry uniformly

across the grain. All the off cuts were retained and planked for use as sarking boards fixed to the outside of the structure to form the underlay for the slates.

The construction of the Hammerbeam roof was put out to competitive tender. In all specification and tender action, we started by looking for local materials and craftsmen, only if we could not obtain suitable materials, sufficient quality or the required experience locally did we look further afield. The construction of the hammerbeam roof was tendered throughout Britain

Strathyre Oak, Log Transportation.   *Sawmill, McConnel Wood Products, Dumfries.*

Carpenter Oak & Woodland Workshop, Frame Fabrication.

Carpenter Oak & Woodland Workshop, Jointed Beams.

and finally awarded to Carpenter Oak & Woodland who undertook the initial frame fabrication off site in their workshops near Chippenham.

The trusses were set out and the joints constructed in the traditional way by setting out the truss geometry on a flat working plane floor and transferring the centre lines by plumb line to the beams set on trestles. The setting out for the roof was complicated by the fact that we had one wall severely out of alignment. The West side of every truss had to be set out individually to match the curve in the wall head, the angle of every joint was also slightly altered as the pitch changed to meet the wall head.

Whilst the process of design, procurement and off site fabrication was going on, the hall was being prepared for construction work. In order to meet the millennium deadline, the programme required construction work to continue through winter months and a temporary envelope was needed for protection.

The temporary envelope was designed to meet a number of criteria. We wanted a dry and secure environment. We wanted to provide a high level working platform. We wanted to maintain public access to the great Hall for as long as possible and we to undertake as little archaeology as possible as it can seriously disrupt any carefully considered work programme.

The temporary structure had a span of over 21 metres and was 26 metres high. Because of the exposure of the site and the need to ensure that the surrounding buildings were safe, the structure and cladding were designed to meet a one in one hundred year storm risk. The design also had to make sure that we could construct the hammerbeam roof without having to move any of the mid-span scaffold. The scaffold had to be set out to match the hammerbeam trusses, which were set out to the original corbel positions. None of the corbel spacings were regular.

The design of the envelope evolved into a structure that was suspended from the upper level windows. This gave us a high level platform and allowed us to let the public into the principal level of the hall whilst we continued work to the upper levels and in the vaults. The structure only came down to ground level at the four corners which meant minimum foundations and minimum archaeology.

Another problem at the castle is the numbers of visitors. Health and safety legislation states that we are not allowed to kill them! As we had limited storage space in the castle, construction materials had to be stored off site, to make matters more difficult we cannot get a standard three tonne truck into the castle, nor can we get any sort of mobile crane. All materials for the hammerbeam roof had to be brought into the castle outside opening hours and in the order it was to be used.

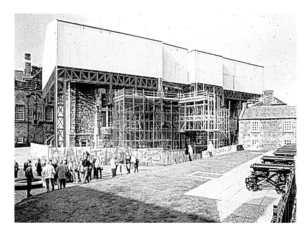

Temporary Envelope.

Construction Materials Delivery

Roof Removal.

Roof Removed

Hammerbeam Construction.

Hammerbeam Construction.

Hammerbeam Joint Detail.

Hammerbeam Joint Detail.

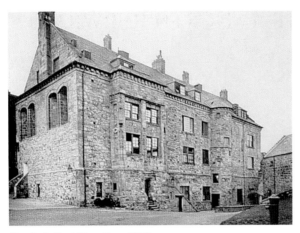

South & East Elevation, 1960s.

South & East Elevation, 1999.

The construction of the hammerbeam roof used 350 oak trees, about 100 cubic metres of timber and some 4000 hand made oak pegs. The work was undertaken by two squads of craftsmen and women working using traditional techniques, apart from the fact that rope pulleys have been replaced by electric hoists. The on site construction from beginning to end took twelve weeks with only a few beams requiring alteration or realignment, the scaffold worked as designed and the structure fitted the bowed wall perfectly.

The restoration was completed to programme and budget, in time for the official opening by the Queen on St Andrew's day 1999, 35 years after the investigations started, in time for the new millennium and the 500th anniversary of its original construction. The total cost, going back to 1964, has not been calculated, but from 1991 to completion the restoration of the Great Hall has cost £8.5 million.

Stirling Castle received a record 430,000 visitors

during the year up to April 2000, and bookings for evening functions in the Great Hall have surpassed all our early estimates. The completion of the Great Hall has involved hundreds of individuals over the years and those of us who had the privilege of completing the project are greatly indebted to all who went before and all who supported us on the way.

Interior, 1970's.   *Interior, 1999.*   *Interior, Evening Function.*

South Elevation, Floodlighting.

Stirling Castle & The Great Hall, from the South.

Heraldic Lion.

SCOTTISH SEABIRD CENTRE, NORTH BERWICK

Sue Whittle, Simpson & Brown Architects

The Centre was conceived as a visitor attraction, where people could study the bird life on the local islands at North Berwick. The idea was to have remote cameras positioned on the islands, sending live pictures to the Centre, so that the public could view the birds without disturbing the colonies. The building, funded by the Millennium Commission, had to be a landmark building for North Berwick.

The original plan was to develop the 1930s Harbour pavilion on the Esplanade. However the restoration and conversion of this proved impractical, and indeed, it was agreed that a purpose-made building was needed. The site itself was a major inspiration for the building. It is situated on a rocky promontory beside the Old Harbour, and it has panoramic views of the Bass Rock, the Isle of May, Craig Rock and Fidra. The amazing all-round views at the high level generated the concept of a circular building with an extended entrance to draw visitors across Anchor Green, from the town centre. The monopitched main roof and entrance roof is generated by the plan. The entrance roof in particular is sculptured to be more dominant and dramatic and define the way in. The spine wall projects along the path to protect visitors from the extremes of the weather, as they enter. The driving wind and salt spray were considerable factors in the modelling of the building. The overhanging eaves and ridges, designed to protect the upper walls and windows, were potentially vulnerable. We designed them to be really sturdy and aerodynamic. I feel we were more influenced by aeroplane structures at the time rather than the flight of birds.

The internal planning is very simple. The shop, reception and restaurant are located on the entrance level, along with the viewing deck. The exhibition and auditorium are on the floor below. The different

functions of the building, on the upper and lower levels, are reflected in the choice of structure and materials.

Having such an exposed location, both the shape and the choice of materials was crucial. Simpson & Brown have a long-running interest in green buildings, and a wealth of knowledge on historic buildings. This knowledge was invaluable to us in the development of the design and specification. We were able to draw on the experience of the partners and associates such as Mandy Ketchin. Mandy has recently been working on the appropriate rural housing project, with Ivor Davies, who is going to speak tomorrow, and has developed prototype pattern books for housing to stimulate the use of home-grown timber in Scotland. We wanted to use natural, real and raw materials and that is why we set out to source local natural materials wherever possible. We have not always been successful but it has been one of our fundamental objectives.

The dry stone wall was inspired very much by the harbour walls in North Berwick, and was chosen for its durability, as well as its wonderful texture and form and colour. The stone was from a local quarry near North Berwick. The battered wall envelops the lower inward-looking exhibition area, and creates a solid base for the more open viewing level. I won't dwell on this part of the building, but get on to the main points of interest for today, the specification and use of timber.

The structure of the upper entrance floor is primarily timber. I counted approximately 8 different timber species, used in the construction of this building. We have used European Larch, Douglas Fir, Redwood, Oak, Beech as well as small quantities of salvage green heart and pitch pine.

We initially considered a European Oak structure for the main structure, but the budget wouldn't really to stretch to that, unfortunately. After careful consideration and advice, we chose green European Larch for the main structure, trusses, columns and beams, as Larch is produced in Britain in sufficient quantities and size. Actually this is English, rather than Scottish timber, I am afraid, but in context this is reasonably local, although we would have preferred it to been grown closer to home. Larch is one of the stronger growths of softwood, but I will let the experts talk about that, and it is moderately durable, having natural resistance to decay, hence its traditional use as fence posts and in boat building. It does not require preservative treatment if detailed properly, and it is relatively inexpensive. Indeed it seems that it has been an undervalued timber until recently. One possible drawback with Green Larch is its tendency to produce shakes as it dries but we don't feel that it detracts from

the overall appearance. The circular form of the building gave us quite a detailing challenge in terms of its structure.

In order to create a relatively open-plan area within the centre of the building, without creating a forest of columns, we designed a system of paired trusses around the void. Each pair stands from one of the 9 central columns, to 2 separate columns on the perimeter. This triangulation strengthened the roof structure by bracing it, but it also gave us some geometrical nightmares. Will Rudd Associates were the structural engineers, and they did a great job making it all work, as did Donaldson McConnell, the timber frame contractors who had the awesome task of manufacturing all the different sizes and types of trusses, and also fitting it all together on site.

Once the main structure was up, the softwood framing and sarking was fitted into place before cellulose insulation was blown into the roof. The wall construction – the upper walls were either fully glazed or clad in timber. The timber clad wall construction is based on a breathing wall system, and as such it is permeable to vapour. The deep eaves and cills are designed to protect the end grain of the timber from weathering, which should improve its longevity. Again, we chose unfinished European Larch hard wood for the rain screen cladding. This first slide shows the 75 x 25-odd boards when they were first fitted. The 75 x 25 timber board when first fitted is a warm, reddish-brown colour. After 3 years' exposure the timber has weathered to a silvery-grey with a wonderful variety of texture. The restaurant balcony is constructed in Larch with recycled green heart columns. The Larch balustrade is constructed in chunky sections for strength, and also with a view to prolonging the service life of the timber. All the fixings are stainless steel to avoid corrosion. The European Oak deck to the balcony was chosen for its durability, both in terms of weather and traffic. It appears to be standing up to the task, although the tannin staining on the stainless steel fixings and concrete columns below had to be washed off for several months after it was fitted. The use of salvaged green heart was suggested for a lintel and the balcony columns, as it is one of the most durable hard woods, and a material, which is often, used historically in piers and sea defences. We have 4 recycled green heart columns supporting the balcony.

The ethic of using salvaged tropical hardwood is open to debate, but its suitability and durability isn't, as far as I am concerned. We used another salvage timber for the external doors. This is pitch Pine. Again, this was selected with durability in mind, but it is also a fine joinery timber, with a beautiful grain. The doors were given a natural oil-based finish for external timber. However, after 3 years of buffeting by weather and visitors, I would say it was time that they were recoated with a more durable finish. This may be why external joinery was traditionally painted, and why we were encouraged to paint the window joinery to prevent adverse weathering. We carried out a lot of research into possible local suppliers of timber windows and sent out a performance specification to a number of Scottish manufacturers. There did not appear to be many local firms who could meet all our objectives, and we ended up choosing windows from a Yorkshire firm, "Environmental Construction Products", who seemed to understand our environmental requirements. Their "Eco-plus" windows were manufactured in Scandinavian Redwood and treated with a boreham-based preservative before being coated with a natural oil-based finish from OS Colour. We asked the manufacturers whether the windows could be made in home-grown European Larch heartwood, but we were told that suitable sections were not available. The windows are outward-opening, and tilt and turn designed for flexibility. Both the small windows at the top and the larger central panel can be opened to allow for ventilation. This shows the window detail within the timber boarding on the restaurant balcony. The Oak sill projects over the timber boarding to protect the end grain of the Larch boarding. The Douglas Fir eaves T+ G boarding was chosen as a plain timber, as it was to be used both internally and externally. At one stage we intended to form the whole ceiling in Douglas Fir boarding but this was omitted during cost saving. I feel this might have looked a little rustic but it would have required a vast amount of fire retardant lacquer to comply with the surface spread of flame regulations. The internal glazed screen balustrade and other joinery were formed in Beech, a traditional British joinery timber, with few knots, warm grain and a fine colour which blends with the other timbers. Even the toilet cubicles are real wood, rather than MDF or anything similar. I feel the painted finish here was more functional, allowing for cleaning and recoating after the inevitable graffiti appears.

Summing up, I have tried to say a little bit about all the timbers specified in the building and now there are the additions of bird boxes. I am really glad that the Centre has been a success, and continues to draw crowds of visitors to North Berwick. I would like to think that the form and materials contributed to the public's appreciation of the Centre.

THE HUB, EDINBURGH

Ben Tindall, Benjamin Tindall Architects

Timber has always been fundamental to Scottish architecture, despite the popular image of stone. The Hub's original design and construction was superb. It really was a Rolls Royce building. The architect was Gillespie Graham, and the detailing of some of the building was Pugin. Pugin seems to get all the credit, but Gillespie Graham was the principal architect. He was a very, very practical architect. He was very high-tech in his own way, in his own age, on his day. The building – Pugin and Gillespie Graham also entered the Houses of Parliament competition. Pugin of course also did it with Barry and won on that horse – he was backing two horses at once – but the quality and construction of this building is actually quite similar in some ways to the Houses of Parliament. It really is fantastic.

A nice view of the building showing Johnston Terrace before anything was built, and Heriot's Hospital there with a wellhead at the top. This shows the building, how it was in 1852. That's 10 years after it was built, and you can see there the layout of the seats in this room – kind of – and there is a popular misconception that this building was a church. It's the spire which does that. It was actually the assembly hall as it says there, and this map shows very clearly the other assembly hall, the Free Church Assembly Hall which is now the Church of Scotland Assembly Hall.

So this building is another parliament building. This really was the church parliament for the annual Assembly. The building got known, as many things, but originally as this say, this superb structure was called Victoria Hall, and going along with Victoria Terrace, Victoria Street, Victoria this and that and there is some very careful wording here which says that the building was opened, I think in the presence of the Queen – i.e. she was passing by in a coach in 1843. The building latterly got known as the Highland Tollbooth or St John's Highland Tollbooth, or any combination of those words. The words of the various congregations that used the building. The Highland congregation was the Gaelic congregation. The Church of Scotland established the church, the Gaelic congregation – the Tolbooth congregation was one of the congregations that came out of St Giles, and this is a photograph of the last General Assembly held in this building, from 1929, and after that the Church of Scotland and the Free Kirk joined together and decided they would go to the Free Kirk's Assembly Hall, which

they thought was a bigger, and better building. I think they would have been better off here. That is 1929 with the Duchess of York, as she was then, and Queen Mother as she became, sitting there with the Duke of York. All the women in the balcony, all the men below.

There is a puzzle in this building that I don't understand. Someone might be able to explain it to me, but there are 2 stairs either side of the stage here, but they go in different asymmetrical directions, and I think it is something to do with access to the gallery, and separation of men and women. The building declined, mirroring the economic decline of the High Street, and church attendance generally. The various congregations that used the place sort of dwindled, and in fact have joined up with Greyfriars across the way, and the building was left empty, still in the hands of the Church of Scotland, and became a huge concern to Historic Scotland, the City and everyone, and a repair scheme was carried out by Stewart Tod & Partners of the building. All the gutters were neglected, and the spire was also wobbling, and really the building was getting into a terrible state and there were many many uses proposed for the building. The last one I think was going to use this room for white-knuckle rides, with catering by Macdonalds underneath. I am sure it would have been very successful. Although some basic repairs were carried out, the building was empty for many many years, looking for a use.

After this time of neglect, we did a very thorough survey of the building, revealing an insignificant piece of woodworm, the only woodworm found in the entire building; the quality of timber was so good.

The rot had been repaired. Sorry, I was going to say that as a practice, established 20 years ago, we have never, ever, used poisons. I think having worked as a carpenter, I really would not want to specify poisons for carpenters to use, or inhabitants to have to put up with. One of our bibles has been a wonderful book on toxic treatments. It talks about things like surveyors who drill a few woodworm flight holes to make a sale; invent new pests that need eradication, including the concrete beetle, for those awkward situations where there are no timber floors to treat. This is a terrible racket. With people like Brian Ridout and Jagjit Singh here, we are in good hands. I am quite surprised that they are still alive, and Rentokil have not had their lives … For 20 years we have always relied on proper ventilation of timbers, proper detailing, as the sensible way of doing things, and the lack of maintenance to the building, in its latter days, the cost of putting that right was absurd, compared with the cost of maintaining it now. The Hub has an annual maintenance contract of such a small amount, it actually defies why such rot was allowed to set in, in the first place. It is ridiculous, and it is a very good building too.

This slide is the key to the design of this project, and the obvious thing to have done would have been to have had offices on the ground floor, where the Church of Scotland had its offices. The café is where the Committee Rooms were. The box office is where the accounting rooms and clerks were. The rooms downstairs all had classical cornices and fireplaces, and they were designed as offices. That would have been the sensible place to have put offices, but in doing so, how would the public get in without all the difficulties of lifts and everything else. So it seemed more important that the public be able to come in straight off the street. That meant the offices had to go somewhere else, and putting the offices in the roof is actually what made this project work.

I will finish – a speaker here will appreciate the motto on the purlins there, the story was done by a Finn, but first of all, there was a very clear brief of what was required, and the question was, could that be fitted into the roof, and with some rearrangement of the structure, we decided it could do. The original roof above us here now, was of superb timber, as I have said; very fine wrought iron connections, and in basically good shape. However, contemporary modern office loads are ridiculous. They basically assume that you will cover the entire floor with filing cabinets, and that must have been the death of so many buildings being converted into offices; it really is an absurd loading. In addition, these trusses here have to hang large loads for presentations, and so forth.

The main problem with the roof – in fact the previous repairs were done by a specialist rot company – and that was the weakest part of the building. We had excellent engineers: Peter Ellis & Company, and we really pushed him very hard to analyse the timber structure – we were determined to keep it timber, and these are some of Peter's excellent drawings that he did of this. The real problem, as we know, as has been said before, was with the connections and with the joints. The original connections were very beautiful but we had to re-design modern connections, which were a great deal stronger. We used original spirit to the original connections. On the left there you will see there are twin sheet-steel, plate-steel connections for the main truss at the foot. These make the trusses immensely strong, and allow you to use the full strength of the timber. The main struts had to be raised, in order to make the space work. This involved a lot of very complicated temporary works; these are the new struts that had to go in. They are actually designed to cope for expansion in the office; in future, you could actually put a mezzanine floor on there as well, and then cellular offices are made at the side, with general open-plan in the centre.

Fantastic views, north and south over the City, the Firth of Forth and Lammermuirs. Detailing of the roof to allow ventilation through the roof, and so far, everything has been looking very, very good indeed.

A couple of extra things. Timber is such a versatile thing, obviously fire resistance has not been talked about yet – downstairs I think you will see the largest fire doors you can find; these don't actually fit in the opening, they fit over the opening. We couldn't get special shape to work, obviously, and lastly, the beauty of timber is always appreciated, even if it is just skin deep and it is paint. And that's what all this is here, I am afraid to say.

HOUSING IN THE HIGHLANDS

Neil Stephen, Dualchas Building Design

Timber-frame kit-houses dominate house building in the Highlands. To many they are, as Prince Charles described, a blot on the landscape. To one architect we met, they demonstrate that Highlanders are cultural philistines.

But if that architect had looked at the reason for the proliferation of the timber kit, rather than insulting a people while throwing up their hands, they would have understood why they are so successful.

Compared to the old stone white house, they are easy to construct, are warm and can be made wind and water-tight quickly. Most importantly, they are relatively cheap, and are geared towards consumers on a tight budget requiring grant assistance. The companies involved also assist with planning applications, warrants and service connections. In fact, the kit-house companies have made themselves popular by providing a package to the consumer that makes building easy.

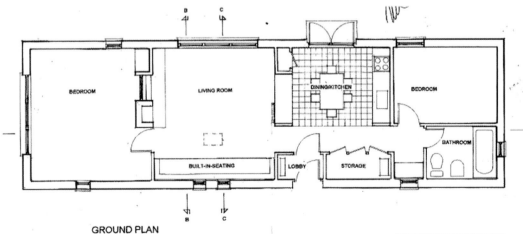

GROUND PLAN

Plan of a Timber framed house designed in the simple form of the long house

Timber frame construction on site

Timber clad offices for a timber supply company

What they do not provide is good design, probably for the reason that they don't have to. We therefore decided to do our own timber frame buildings based on the simple form of the long house, the indigenous building type of the Highlands, while trying to offer all the services and more of the kit-house company.

Initially this required us to be proactive in the community, in persuading people to take what they perceived to be a risk. A friend took the plunge, and our first house was built for £35,000 using a Scottish Homes grant. The design expressed a simple form which sits easily in the landscape, yet is interesting in its planning and volume internally.

This house, and many which followed, have rendered walls and slate roofs. For a number of years, this has been the design mantra of many planning officials, who feel that these materials are key to keeping a building in the rural highlands traditional. A proposed timber clad building often met with disapproval, except in isolated circumstances.

Fortunately for us, and to the credit of the Scottish Parliament, the book *Timber Cladding in Scotland* was recently published. This led to our local planning officer taking a family holiday to Norway, and he is now much more sympathetic. Much to the credit of planning departments in the Highlands there appears to be a willingness to take on new ideas and move away from the obsession with render and slate. Whether the planning departments of the east coast of Scotland move from their obsession with Fyfe stone and pantiles is another matter.

In any case, at Dualchas we now have several timber clad buildings on the drawing board, on Lewis, in Argyll, and on Skye. These are being done from our larch-clad office in Sleat.

However, it is pointless to talk about housing in the Highlands, whether timber clad or not, without mentioning the fundamental problem; the lack of affordable land.

As one Gaelic teacher from Lochaber told me, after a fruitless search for a house plot for him and his young family " the one thing the Highlands lacks is people, and the one thing we have is land, and yet it would cost me £60,000 to buy a quarter acre plot in the place where I was brought up."

This situation is, of course, absurd and there are two main reasons for it.

Firstly, planning policy. According to the local plan for Skye and Lochalsh, there is a surplus of land for housing development. A rendered map, which shows areas where house development is permitted, designates this.

Unfortunately, this bears no relationship to the reality on the ground. Much of this designated land is not, and possibly never will be, available for house building. Other areas, which may be available, are rendered the wrong colour on the map. Meanwhile local estate agents reveal that plots of land in south Skye, which would have cost £12,000 five years ago, are now being valued at £30,000. A recent report in the West Highland Free Press showed that Skye and Lochalsh has the worst housing shortage and levels of homelessness in the Highlands.

The second problem is land ownership. Under the guise of preserving the environment, landowners are either stagnating or destroying local communities. In Sleat, where I live, the Clan Donald Estate will not release any land for housing, as their mission statement is to preserve the land as it was in the time of their forebears, one hundred and fifty years ago. These fourth generation Americans fail to see the irony in the fact that 150 years ago, 3000 people lived in the community and there are now only 700.

Unfortunately, the much-vaunted land reform bill of the Scottish parliament will do little to resolve the situation. Only when land comes on the market will communities be entitled to bid for it in attempt to take control. As experience shows that this will be a rare occurence, most of rural Scotland will be left unaffected, and no better off.

Yet while large landowners come in for criticism, with considerable justification, there is little said about the

role of crofters in developing communities. It is often the case that in crofting areas the common grazing is the prime land for development. This land used to be seen as common land for the good of the whole community, but it is now under the control of the crofters only, who make up a fraction of the local population.

Has timber a sustainable future in the Highlands of Scotland

View of lobby with patent glazing

While some crofting communities are forward looking and do exploit this resource, others are content to do nothing. I know of one case where the crofters will not even release a quarter acre of land for a much-needed local shop, and in doing so oppose the expressed wishes of the vast majority of the community.

Surely the Crofting Commission should address this problem by refocusing their view of land from agricultural asset to development asset. Crofting tenure was, after all, brought in to allow people to remain on the land, and if it is now doing the opposite, then something is seriously wrong. And as the latest census figures demonstrates, the number of young people living in the Highlands is plummeting, with houses and plots being bought up by the cash-rich over fifty-fives.

Is this important to a conference on timber and the built environment? Absolutely, as if these issues are not addressed, architects will have few opportunities to put their ideas in to practice. We can talk about planting trees and using sustainable timber technology, but if people cannot get land to build, then architecture becomes irrelevant. The current situation is not only bad for the rural building industry, but can be disastrous for the development of rural economies.

Therefore we should praise the Scottish Parliament for its interest in design, but criticise the toothless land reform bill which will have little or no impact on the vast majority of rural communities. And we should say that it is good that planning policy is being encouraged to accept timber clad buildings, but wrong that there are so many restrictions to housing development in place.

I think it should be the role of the architect to be politicised, and take on these issues. It is up to us to show that housing need not be a blot on the landscape, and that the Highlands should be a breathing, vibrant community, and not merely a playground for toffs.

THE USE OF UNTREATED SCOTTISH TIMBER AT THE GLENCOE VISITOR CENTRE

C Morgan, Gaia Architects

Introduction

Gaia Architects recently completed the Glencoe Visitor Centre for the National Trust for Scotland (NTS). The building is possibly the 'greenest' major building in Scotland and is built entirely out of Scottish timber without the use of chemical treatments.

This paper is divided into 3 main sections. The first provides some brief context for the project itself and Gaia's understanding of ecological design. This sets the scene for the second section, which looks in more detail at the issues of specifying timber within an ecological design framework. The third section discusses how these principles of timber specification were applied at Glencoe.

Context

The Project

Gaia was first appointed in 1994 by the National Trust for Scotland to design the new Visitor Facilities at Glencoe. The decision to remove the existing Centre had been taken in 1991 and the new site earmarked for the new Visitor Facilities was the Inverigan Caravan Site, previously owned by the Forestry Commission.

After a lengthy process of both Client and local community consultation, coupled with frustrations in finding funding, the project started on site in 2000 with three separate contracts for the infrastructure works, the main building, and the demolition and re naturalisation of the existing site. The Visitor Centre opened in May 2002.

Ecological Design at Glencoe

The brief for the building was explicitly 'green', as understood by the NTS and this was developed by Gaia under four headings:

- Site
- Resources
- Energy
- Health

Site

Overall, the Visitor Centre comprises around 1200 m² of new buildings, but instead of one large block, it was designed as a series of domestic scale buildings sited loosely around and within existing trees. This strategy allowed the landscape to remain the 'star of the show', while the buildings fitted in better with the landscape, without the loss of many trees.

The paradox faced by the NTS and, in microcosm, by this project, is how to protect the landscape from the very visitors the Centre aimed to encourage. Apart from producing a 'green' building, Gaia's response was to make conscious this paradox through the deliberate and careful location of the buildings within the landscape, and by the way in which visitors' experience the landscape as they move between buildings. Access to all buildings is via external boardwalks that were used as a mechanism to 'remove' the visitor from the adjacent, untouched groundscape and flora. Trees were retained - sometimes inconveniently so for the visitor - all to affect an awareness of what was there before and the tricky issue of how to "rub" along together with nature.

A stream which was previously diverted has been reinstated and runs through the middle of the complex acting as an open drain for all rain and surface water outlets and enlivening the courtyard with the sound of running water. Access to all areas is level.

Resources

Essentially the single most effective technique to reduce the ecological footprint of buildings is to ensure that new buildings are flexible and can be used without prejudice for generations.

The subsequent principal is one of layering the construction to enable the easy modification or refurbishment of outer layers without affecting the layers beneath. At Glencoe we used timber portal frames so that partitions could be moved or removed, as the Client needed while all floors walls and surfaces conceal a service void, giving the Client freedom to route future services. A complementary approach to fixings, whereby components were either screwed or bolted was also developed so all can be readily removed for maintenance, repair or replacement.

Other details evolved to produce a building that is recyclable in practice, not just in theory. It is much easier to repair, re-use or recycle single material components so we used timber in preference to particleboard, for example, and avoided anything that was bonded to anything or coated with anything, because it is unlikely ever to be worth someone's while to recover it.

We engaged specialist expertise to ensure that our designs represented best practice in sewage treatment and water conservation with low flush imported toilets, waterless urinals, aerating taps, reduced dead legs and a number of other small improvements upon conventional practice.

Energy

Energy efficiency can be considered both in terms of operational efficiencies and the embodied energy of the materials which make up a building.

At it's simplest, reducing the embodied energy of the building involves reducing the quantities of materials involved, by design. For example we reduced the amount of concrete in the foundations by using pads rather than trenches or rafts. Otherwise, materials used were largely natural with relatively simple manufacturing processes.

In terms of operational energy efficiencies, the most important thing by far is conservation. In this way we directed our attentions first to insulation. The 250mm portal frames are fully filled recycled newsprint insulation to floors, walls and ceilings. Extremely low heating costs are therefore achieved.

Lastly, we used a wood-chip fired Finnish boiler to heat a district heating system which connected all the buildings, including showers in the (to be) refurbished Caravan Site Ablutions Block. By succeeding in getting the whole complex wood-chip heated, we achieved a carbon neutral heated development at a stroke. A local company who sources the chip from nearby forest waste provided the expertise.

Health

Healthy building design involves reducing pollution - from materials and from processes, and then attempting to create the ideal internal environment in terms of temperature, moisture and so on.

The first step is to reduce the amount of toxic materials introduced into the environment. In a building built largely of timber, the most insidious of these are timber preservatives. Glues were kept to a minimum - the only use being to hold down the linoleum. Materials in general were natural. No PVC was used, with plastics and other petrochemical derivatives kept to a minimum. All finishes were plant based.

Almost all of the buildings are naturally ventilated, with extract ventilation only in places of high air change requirements. All parts of the fabric, walls,

floors and ceilings, are of 'breathable' construction.

That is to say, moisture transfusive with intrinsic protection against interstitial condensation and mould. We aimed to create a balanced climate in terms of relative humidity, keeping

it between 40 and 60 percent because of the health risks which develop at both extremes of relative humidity. Passive design aims to regulate this by using the fabric of the building itself so all materials used were hygroscopic, capable of absorbing and releasing vapour to a certain degree.

The Ecological Design of Timber

Timber is often used by Designers to impart a sort of 'green' aesthetic to a building and, for good and ill, this aesthetic is enjoying a degree of popularity at present. However, if one digs a little deeper, it is too often the case that this timber is imported from old growth Canadian (and now Siberian) or non-sustainably managed forests. The timber is impregnated with arsenic compounds, detailed badly so that it will not last longer than 10 years and will then officially represent toxic waste when it is prematurely replaced. For an environmentalist this is a tragedy, and does nothing to further the cause of responsible timber specification, nor of the forestry interests in Scotland.

The ecological specification of timber, we would argue, may be defined under four headings:

1. Sourced from responsibly managed forests

2. Sourced from as close to home as is practical, UK sourced at least

3. Free from chemical impregnation and toxic and impermeable coatings

4. Detailed to be durable, maintainable and easily re-usable / replaceable

If this is achieved, then throughout its life, the timber will be a positive benefit to the local economy and ecology, not simply a reduced problem. It will not cause pollution before, during or after its intended lifespan and may positively benefit the health of the occupants during its time in place and so be cost effective for the Client. In other words it will be part of, and perhaps help initiate a sustainable construction industry, not simply a less unsustainable one.

The first of these points is self explanatory and moreover is covered, in this case, by the second, the reasons for which are as follows:

The world wide timber industry is vast and complex and, despite the concerted efforts of a few organisations, it is difficult to confidently certify timber from abroad as genuinely sustainable. Specifying local timber allows us much greater control

Glencoe Visitor Centre for the National Trust for Scotland

over, and thus confidence in, the sources and suppliers of the timber used.

Using timber from nearby sources reduces the transport requirements of a project with obvious environmental benefits. Using local timber suppliers directly supports the local economy with indirect benefits across the local community. The Scottish timber industry is greatly undervalued with a significant potential that can be realised by doing this.

Supporting the local timber industry in this way help to increase the viability of local woodlands, which, again indirectly, benefits the local environment and community.

The third point - the need to develop durable design solutions without the need for chemicals is perhaps the least widely appreciated aspect of what we consider to be ecological design. It is as if the notions of durability and synthetic ('maintenance free') materials have become synonymous in the minds of many, but the evidence of the legacy of old buildings built of entirely natural materials reveals the paucity of this idea. There is no doubt as to the many health risks posed by the materials and coatings with which we now create our architecture, but somehow the message does not get through.

The health of occupants of buildings is of prime concern to Gaia, and we try to create healthy spaces by:

The avoidance of chemical preservative pre-treatment, through a coordinated strategy of timber species choice and detailing and by not introducing known toxic materials or coatings throughout the building as far as is practically possible.

The careful choice of coatings such that the vapour porous materials and surfaces used can regulate the internal humidity of the spaces as noted above.

The reasons for the fourth point are also self-explanatory and the implementation of this is discussed in more detail in the following section.

The Use of Timber at Glencoe

In designing the timber at Glencoe we borrowed not only on our own experience of timber design in Scotland, developed over a number of years with various "eco-houses" and the like, we also gained much from our Norwegian colleagues. Norwegian timber construction traditions have informed much of our apparently innovative (to the UK) design ideas!

To further develop our thinking on timber specification and the Scottish context, we worked closely with

The Visitor Centre is carefully placed within the landscape

Bernard Planterose of North Woods Construction, establishing a hierarchy of hazard classes and preferred specification options for each anticipated timber use in the building.

Overall, we tried to use timber for as much as possible, by volume, and in so doing create a sort of informal demonstration project of the potential of the Scottish timber industry at large. Although in many cases the cost of the Scottish timber was more expensive, by trying to match what we wanted to what we knew could be easily supplied, by minimising the machining required, by removing the costs associated with pre-treatment and other manoeuvres, we kept the costs within acceptable tolerances.

Main Structural Members

The whole building is raised off the ground on steel beams, which span between pads, allowing ventilation under the floors and ground water to run unhindered across the site. The main structure is of timber portal frames that allow all internal walls to be moved or removed at will, so increasing the flexibility and thus durability of the internal spaces.

All structural timbers needed to be stress graded to C18, which lies above the normal C16 to which homegrown spruce is normally graded in Scotland, therefore the natural choice appeared to be Douglas fir. It transpired during the design process that Scottish sourced Douglas Fir could not be graded to the same strength as imported Fir, but ironically the final species choice by the Contractor was spruce, graded as specified.

The frames, embedded within the insulation, did not need to be treated because of the vapour permeability of the 'breathing wall' construction, and the hygroscopicity of the recycled paper insulation chosen. This would not have been the case if standard timber frame technique and mineral fibres had been used.

Internal Secondary Structure and Battens

Internal partition structure and battening generally was not prey to excessive moisture and risk of decay and could thus be of any softwood. Cheap whitewood was specified and the exact nature and source of the timber used (as long as it was from Scotland) was left to the Contractor to enable him to keep costs down. Spruce was used.

Roof and Wall Cladding

With the notable exception of the hut on the top of Ben Nevis there are few Scottish examples of timber roof boarding. Apart from hardwood timbers such as Chestnut, Elm and Oak, not readily (or cheaply) available in Scotland, the only contender for external

cladding with accepted durability was heartwood of European Larch. Douglas Fir was arguably as good, but less reliably so.

We opted for a rough sawn surface for both wall and roof cladding boards because it increases the rate of evaporation of moisture from the open surface texture. The open surface texture also protects the timber marginally better against UV degradation and therefore less readily forming minor surface cracks. The cladding is the only place where elements were nailed, because it was agreed that boards needing removal would not be re-used. Care was taken to establish the torque of the nail guns to avoid the nail head penetrating beyond the board surface and exposing end grain. The battens supporting the cladding boards required to be heartwood of larch as well, being subject to largely the same climatic conditions. Sarking boards used under the slate roofs were of sawn spruce, safe from decay because of ventilation beneath and a vapour permeable membrane above.

Flooring

The only homegrown hardwoods in the British Standard for heavy traffic (>2000 people per day) are Oak, Beech and Hornbeam. The two latter timbers are not readily available in the quality and quantity required, however oak floorboards could be supplied from Highland sources. Some of the oak sourced came from the Altyre Estate near Forres, where it had lain since it was blown over in storms back in 1952, yet was as good as new when machined.

We developed a detail for floorboards using short T&G boards with rebated ends held down by a timber strip screwed to the battens below. The boards themselves are not fixed down at all, so that when the cover strip is unscrewed and removed, the boards can be simply lifted out. We ran these along the lengths of the buildings to correlate with main service runs so that access could not be easier. Anyone who has ever de-nailed old floorboards will appreciate the value of this detail!

The short lengths of board also dovetailed into the advice we received from the Scottish timber industry that short lengths could be much more easily sourced. In fact, it turned out that some suppliers would have preferred random lengths - this more closely relating to what could be efficiently extracted from the timber stock, so we altered the detail in some places to ease the task of sourcing so much timber.

Elsewhere we had originally specified birch, but there were last minute problems sourcing it and we opted instead for Sycamore - all that appeared to be available at the time - in some of the less trafficked areas. In the Staff areas we used Scots Pine.

Internal Ceiling Linings

This was detailed in much the same way as the flooring boards but without the need for rebated boards and flush cover strips. A timber that finishes well was sought and the light colour of birch, its correspondence with the many birch trees outside, and the desire to promote the use of this most abundant of native species made it the first choice for the timber ceiling in the Cafe. It had to be painted, uniquely, with an intumescent coating for fire reasons that unfortunately detracted from its ability to regulate indoor air climate.

Doors and Windows

A notable achievement of the project was the use of Scottish oak for all external joinery. Despite dire warnings from many that this was not achievable the products have performed well. Equally difficult to achieve were internal doors to a cost even remotely approaching the conventional cardboard wafer, ply veneered norm. After a couple of false starts, it was achieved by a combination of extremely simple detailing and by flexibility in the species allowable. The timbers were a mix of alder, birch ash and others. This enabled him to use what was available, and the results were of a high quality.

Wood fuel

The use of wood as a fuel fitted exactly our ecological brief and intentions. We used a 120 kW boiler to feed the Centre and the adjacent Caravan Site Ablutions block via a district heating system.

A local company, Torren Energy, from forest brash in nearby Forestry Commission forests supplied the woodchip. Torren also maintain the boiler and associated plant.

Project Contacts:

Client:	National Trust for Scotland, Inverness
Architect:	Gaia Architects, Edinburgh
Landscaping:	Gaia Architects, Edinburgh
Main Contractor:	R J McLeod, Dingwall
Quantity Surveyor:	Ralph Ogg & Partners, Perth
Structural Engineer:	John Peden Associates, Oban
Interpretation:	Studioarc, Edinburgh
Internal Fit-Out	(Kitchen Fit-Out by NTS)

WOOD AS A DESIGN MATERIAL

Ivor Davies

Over the next half-hour, I am going to give a slightly idiosyncratic tour of the use of timber as a designer's material.

Yesterday we saw some great examples of timber being used in contemporary construction, and we probably heard that it was not always that easy to source the raw materials. Today, I want to turn that discussion round and look at using Scottish material, from the producers' viewpoint. Any discussion of timber in Scotland has to start by acknowledging the importance of timber frame.

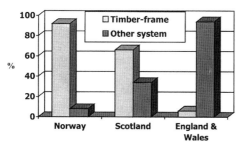

Figure 1: % Market share for timber-frame construction in low-rise housing

Here we can see the market share for timber frame construction in low-rise housing in Scotland, Norway and England and Wales. So the yellow is timber frame construction, and the blue is other structural systems. As you can see, Norway has got slightly over 90% of low-rise housing as timber frame. In England and Wales it is only about 6%. Scotland is much nearer towards Norway than it is to England and Wales, in terms of the market share. Timber frame is a major success story in Scotland. It is, however, a success story that is almost invisible to the average customer, because as you know, we build all our houses out of timber, then we hide them behind the structural skin of breeze blocks, and pretend we all live in stone houses. Any discussion of the supply of timber has to start at the sawmill. That is where the story really starts.

There are three scales of sawmill: most construction timber comes from an automated mill. The operator there staring at his Star Trek-like screens can produce mind-blowing quantities of timber, and do it really almost single-handedly. It is a very efficient operation. There are also a few medium-sized sawmills and quite a number of small sawmills. These medium and small mills are not really producing the kind of structural timber that most of you are familiar with. Instead they are looking at more specialised products, often outside the construction industry, but sometimes they are doing things like these visually stress graded timber; maybe some of the joinery products you can see at the back, and so on. Timber frame uses fairly short graded timbers, like this. As you probably know, there are two types of strength grading. There is machine strength grading, and also visual grading. Machine grading, each piece of timber is individually assessed and then automatically assigned to the relevant strength class. It is thus a form of objective quality assurance, and machine-graded timber of a strength class from Scotland will be sold on a fit-for-purpose basis. It is interchangeable with strength-graded timber of the same strength class from anywhere else. The other type of strength grading is for buildings like this, as you saw with Stirling Castle yesterday. It is visually graded as opposed to going through a machine. This is just to emphasise the kind of defect that affects the strength grade. These are the knots. The other main defect is spiral grain, which reduces the strength of the timber. Difficult to see, but I put this slide in and if Richard Harris is in the audience, just to show that Scotland can also produce really spectacular grid shells in timber. This is a little lean-to in the back of a sawmill on Skye, and you can see that the very straight grains, knot-free timber here, is a small, but nonetheless, quite a spectacular little structure. I should say that the machine strength graded timber you can get in Scotland is normally only available at C16 grade. Exceptionally you can get slightly higher grades than that.

There is strong timber available in Scotland, but at the moment, it is not economic for the sawmills to separate it out. There are on going discussions and it may be possible to source higher than C16 in the future. After strength, the next most important timber characteristic to consider when designing timber is its moisture content. Nowadays, most timber is dried in large heated chambers in a kiln drying operation. The aim in drying timber is to reduce the moisture to roughly the same as the environment in which it will be used. Moisture affects strength, machining characteristics, durability and also shrinkage and swelling. When a log is freshly felled, it has got quite a high moisture content. As it dries out, it will tend to shrink. It will not shrink very much along the length of the log, however it will shrink around the circumference, and the shrinkage round the circumference is usually about twice of the shrinkage along the radius, and that is why timber splits as it dries. Timber, if it is more than about 100 millimetre thick, will not dry uniformly, so an engineer will always calculate the strength of a thick piece of timber as if the timber has got a high moisture content. It will then shrink as it is installed in the building, and design has to take account of that shrinkage. Norwegian manufacturers will run a saw cut along a piece of timber for log building. Experience has shown that the resultant inevitable splitting will then be concentrated on this line. This side will be hidden in the final building and the exposed face will be split free.

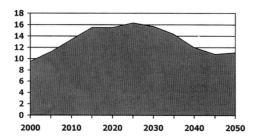

Figure 2: Timber production forecast for the UK over the next fifty years (in millions of cubic metres)

Investment decisions are being driven by production forecasts. This graph shows the amount of timber that is going to be coming out of UK forests over the next 50 years. At the moment there is something like 9 million cubic metres per annum being produced, but over the next 20 years, that figure is going to virtually double. If you have ever wondered what foresters dream about at night, what keeps them awake, it is probably this graph, because this represents a serious challenge for the future. What this graph does not show, is that the bulk of this timber will be medium to low-grade softwoods, the bulk of this increase, and therefore the challenge is to find markets within the construction industry for these types of products. I should say that at the moment, probably only 22% of UK timber is sold into construction. The rest goes into fencing, packaging, and so on. This market is declining and the forestry and the saw milling industry must find more construction-based markets. Markets for quite low-grade timber. Consequently, engineered products are now all the rage. These are two engineered wood products. Howard mentioned one other yesterday, Brenchstappple. These two products are LVL – Laminated Veneer Lumber and also high beams – high joists. LVL is made from lots of sheets of veneer that are glued together into a large structural beam. Effectively, it is a thick piece of plywood. James Jones near Inverness manufactures a similar product in Scotland. These products are a major success story in Scotland and it is hoped that more Scottish timber is used in the future. The production facilities and

processes are doubling capacity and there are plans afoot to triple the capacity in the not-too-distant future. These high joists are now licensed for use as struts and rafters and, as you can see in this general view of the factory, the products are available in very, very long lengths. The other engineered wood product we are probably going to see in the not-too-distant future are large prefabricated structural panels. For example the wall of a caravan has timber composite panels with a strong structural performance. These kinds of products, delivered with factory standards of Quality Assurance, will be available in the not too distant future in Scotland for housing.

The third most important issue we need to think about in designing with timber is durability. The two main risks, are fungal decay and insect attack. It is important to remember that heartwood is much more durable than sapwood. The heartwood of a piece of sweet chestnut – is slightly more durable than Oak. But after only a few months in my yard the sapwood has started to deteriorate. All sapwood of all species should be regarded as being less durable than the heartwood. Durability and wood preservation attracts a very strong, and often conflicting, viewpoints. I wonder if we could just talk about a few of those issues now. Quite often when I go on to building sites, I see preserved and treated timber that has been crosscut and the end grain has not been coated with preservative. If you cross cut a piece of preserved treated timber, and you don't then protect the ends, the envelope of protection is compromised, and most of the value of that wood preservation is lost. I was really struck yesterday that the building conservation world is much further ahead in terms of thinking about durability and preservation than new build. We have in new build, an enormous amount to learn from building conservation. If building conservation can stand up say chemicals are largely irrelevant to wood preservation, think how much easier it could be to control the moisture content of a new build structure. We understand the physics of new build wall sections very well. We can effect environmental control very easily. So, if building conservationists can say why do we need preservatives, then that is relevant to new build as well.

We over-use wood preservatives in the UK. There is no doubt of that, and I think it is significant that over half of the CCA (copper, chromium and arsenic) used in Europe, is used in the British Isles. How do we reduce the use of preservative? We need to look at the technology of grading and detailing of timber very seriously.

In the Faeroes a piece of tropical hardwood relies on natural durability to hold the cladding together and yet, it is covered with sapwood. This cladding will fail, and if you want to avoid wood preservation, you have to do better than this. Although this cladding has a cavity behind it, water is pooling at the base. If God is in the details, she is getting pretty wet at this point. The transfer of timber technology from one country to another is also, I think, a serious problem.

Here we have vertical cladding on a Scandinavian barn. It works perfectly well. It has been around for hundreds of years. However, if you transfer this technology to a modern building, you will generally have problems. A lot of water could penetrate but there is plenty of drainage and ventilation, so there aren't any difficulties. On a modern building, with some breathing membrane behind, drainage and ventilation is restricted and this type of cladding attracts quite a number of problems. Exposure to sunlight will very quickly rot even the best modern breather membrane. Yet despite a very well documented history of the failures of this type of cladding, it is still regularly proposed, and this is playing directly into the hands of people who say that you have to use wood preservation. Therefore to avoid wood preservation the design and technology of timber must be seriously considered.

What timber can we source in Scotland? Spruce is certainly the main construction timber. You can buy it as machine graded structural timber and as sarking. It is available from the very big automated sawmills, and if you want to buy Scottish Spruce, telephone the UK Forest Products Association in Stirling, and they should be able to point you to a suitable supplier. There are three Larch species available in Scotland. European Larch is the one that is most commonly encountered in Scotland and used quite extensively for visually graded structural timber. Douglas Fir is also used for structure and cladding and a structural grade Scottish Oak is readily available. These products are available through members of the UK Forest Products Association, the sort of medium size and smaller sawmills, and you can also source some of these products through the Association of Scottish Hardwood Sawmills. Oak is also very suitable for cladding. Home-grown Oak known as Green Oak is normally sold unseasoned for cladding. The unseasoned Green Oak will shrink. It will shrink probably by about 7% as it dries, and detailing has to take account of that. Therefore, home-grown Oak probably is not suitable for all types of cladding but can be very suitable for flooring. (interior of the house by Robin Webster, which I showed a few slides back) All the timber in this building, apart from the windows, was sourced in Scotland, but mostly in the Highlands. Note also the use of Scots Pine linings. The quality of the timber, the detailing, and the construction in this little house really sing, and I think it is a considerable tribute to the designer, the suppliers and the contractors. You can also source other timbers for flooring. This is Elm. It is not available in huge volumes, none of these species are, but if you want to make a real statement, and you don't mind waiting slightly longer, these sorts of floors in Oak, Ash, Elm, Birch, Sycamore can make quite a cost-effective, and a very spectacular floor.

One of the things of this conference is learning from the past, and I want to identify just a couple of issues where I think we can learn from previous experience in Scotland. The first is grading of knots for external cladding. If you look at the Scots Pine tree, you will see that the branches are all sloping up at an angle, and typically an angle of something like 30 degrees. These branches will go on into the tree at the same kind of angle as knots. This is a piece of vertical cladding from a late 19th century building in Strathspey. This knot is sloping up at an angle of 30 degrees from the outside of the building to the inside. In the days before modern rainscreen cladding, these types of details were very important and they are still included in the recommendations for cladding detail in Scandinavia, or at least in Norway. I have surveyed quite a few Victorian timber clad buildings in Scotland, and somewhere between 70% and 80% of the cladding exhibits this form of grading. The contractor has gone to a lot of work to grade this, so that the knots don't provide an entry point for water. The same type of grading isn't, however, suitable with softwood cladding. Here we can see the end of a log, and the branches, the knots coming out in the typical star pattern. If you imagine trying to cut a board from here, no matter where you cut the board, you will get one knot running up, and one knot running down. It is impossible to avoid that kind of water route, and that is probably one of the main reasons why vertical cladding is more common in our wet maritime climate of Scotland, than horizontal cladding. This type of detailing is less important nowadays with a rainscreen, with a ventilated cavity behind it. Nonetheless, I think it is an issue that could be valuable in some cases, on very exposed sites.

And my last slide is Swiss Cottage. Many of you will have heard me enthuse about Swiss Cottage before. It is a little building that was constructed somewhere between 1820 and 1830, near Fochabers. It was lived in until about 7 years ago. It is now standing empty, and it is beginning to decline. For contemporary designers, this building is important for a number of reasons. First of all, it is made from local Scots Pine. It is made completely from timber, from the Duke of Gordon's Estates in Strathspey. It is not particularly good quality timber. As you can see, there are fairly big knots in it. There is also sapwood all over the place, and yet, despite that, the building has lasted very well. There is virtually no insect attack on this building at all. There are a few bits of decay, but this has only come in the last 5 years, since the building has been

Swiss Cottage, near Fochabers

neglected, and this sort of stuff is very minor, and would be very easily solved, with a bit of replacement and environmental management. The reason it has lasted so well, even though it is not durable timber in any case, is that it is very well detailed for durability. It has got large eaves, and there is no ground contact and, of course, in common with normal Scandinavian practice, it has been given a moisture vapour permeable for water repellent surface coating. In this case, lead paint. And it highlights that relatively low durability timber – and I am thinking here particularly of Scottish Spruce – would be very suitable for these sorts of products, if they are designed and detailed

properly. Swiss Cottage is now standing empty. There have been a number of attempts to secure its future in the last 5 years. As yet, none of them have been successful.

So since we have got some Historic Scotland, and some other very influential people in the audience, I cannot resist concluding by saying that I think we need to be celebrating Scottish timber traditions more than we do. And I cannot think of a better example than this little building. Its future desperately needs securing, and I hope that between us, we can do something about that in the not too distant future.

SIBELIUS HALL

Hannu Tikka, Artto Palo Rossi Tikka Architects

By way of an introduction to the Sibelius Concert Hall in Helsinki, let me give you a background to the project. The project was an open competition for European architects, and part of the brief was to use wood in some way in the construction. In addition, with a budget of just £12million - which in Helsinki does not go far - and a relatively short timescale, the project was a challenging one.

Wood is well known for it's acoustic qualities and is often used in the interiors of buildings, but myself and my partners decided to design a concert hall made as much as possible from wood. There were major uncertainties with this approach since we had little experience or knowledge of using wood on this scale.

Inevitably, we had to use other materials to some extent – the problem with wooden constructions is that with the pressure of the wind outside, they start to move and can make a noise of their own. It was therefore necessary to use concrete staircases and a huge concrete wall on the front of the building.

The hall is built on the site of several old industrial buildings and incorporates an old brick factory. The building consists of the concert hall, a conference wing, the old brick factory area, and an area named 'forest hall', which, with its huge window, was intended as a sort of Finnish metaphor of open space and pine forest. Originally, we wanted to use 200 year-old pine trunks from Lapland in the construction of the

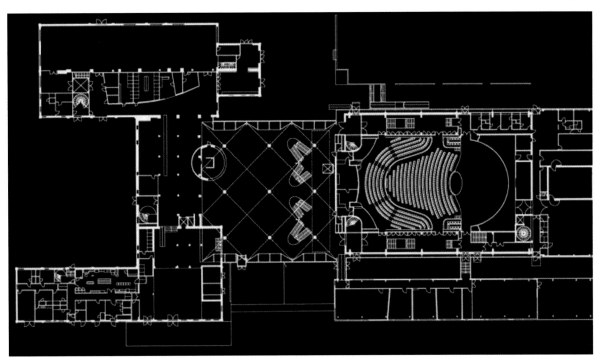

Plan of Sibelius Hall

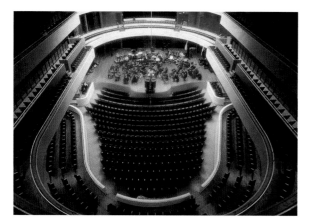

The Concert Hall interior

The Concert Hall at night

forest hall, but there were questions over the strength of these, so we had to resort to using laminated wood. For the inside of the concert hall, the American acoustician Russell Johnston was consulted. Conventionally, it is the architect who draws the layout for a building, but in this case the lines of the building come directly from the acoustician – in fact, our original plans had to be completely revised to accommodate them. The resulting layout is actually better than our original design, and despite the huge space there is a feeling of intimacy. The design also had to take into account the potential for noise pollution from outside since wood is a fairly light material, and so the wall structures are very complicated and have air spaces to reduce the noise. As you move through the building there is a great deal of contrast – from the tiny surroundings of the entrance area to the grandeur of the forest hall and concert hall. The original idea was to use various types of wood for the different areas of the building, again to give a contrast. Although we couldn't fully achieve this, we have used Birch, Spruce, and of course laminated Finnish Pine.

When designing this building, we took inspiration from Gothic structures and attempted to translate something from very beautiful Gothic construction into modern wooden architecture. However, inevitably it may look a little clumsy because of the massive wooden constructions – for example, one of the walls of the concert hall consists of 20 prefabricated wooden structures, each 9 metres by 1.8 metres and weighing 7 tons. However, we feel the plainness of the wooden structures works well because it is a multi-purpose venue – it hosts rock concerts, conferences and classical music events – and so everyone who comes here can feel comfortable in the building. We were also responsible for designing the furniture, which again is fairly plain-looking but was actually quite difficult to make.

The design of the concert hall is in fact a box within a box – the wooden walls of the hall are contained within an outside glass shell, and this is very effective at insulating the sound. Another special feature of the concert hall is the huge 30 ton acoustical canopy straddling over the orchestral area.

At night time, lighting is used to bring out the best in the wood – it can look a bit grey in some weather – and it makes it look very beautiful. I think the Sibelius Hall is a good example of how we can make very big buildings out of wood, and wood is an excellent material because of course it not only looks beautiful but is also nice to touch.

The timber wall construction of the reverberation chambers and the Concert Hall

OSLO AIRPORT TERMINAL

Ole Wiig, Narud-Stokke-Wiig

The old Oslo airport was located south of Oslo and its presence had a severe impact on the local community, so a decision was made to locate the new airport north of the City. It is 47 km north of the city – quite a long way. A very controversial site in that it affected agricultural land with the potential for pollution and it was a long way out of Oslo.

Finally the airport design was opened up to a competition and our submission won. The building was finished in 1998, 4 years ago. It was for a complete new airport, international and national for Oslo. It consisted of a terminal building, flight tower and a railway station. The latter was probably one of the most important issues because at a 47 km distance, you have to make sure you can bring people in quickly and easily. And a special train service was set up like the Heathrow Express which takes you from the city centre of Oslo to the airport in 19 minutes. There is a train running every 10 minutes. You are brought straight into the actual terminal building. You walk straight up, ascend the escalator and you are straight onto your gate.

Gardermoen Airport approach road

The intermediate level, inside the big volume, is the departure level, and that connects onto the flight bridges, and onto the aeroplanes. When you arrive, the airside is on the right hand side and the landside the left. You arrive on the upper level, then you are taken straight down and you find your luggage on the bottom floor, and out you go. So you have separate incoming and outgoing passengers, and that has become more important recently because of security. When you leave Norway you should be on mother soil. You should be on the rocks. So at the very bottom it is actually a stone floor. The next level up, when you arrive you come onto the rock, when you depart you are on a timber shelf. Light. You are out. You are optimistic, and also the section is done that way – the roof opens up, and the glass wall is 26mm tall and 165 metres long. It is all glass. You are leaving the country, leaving the city, and going out into the world. On the very top we designed a steel roof, and we want that to be the progression; to the stone, to the timber, to the steel. The latter we have had to change, because the government had said that the Norwegian timber industry – a very strong lobby – would like to demonstrate the best of Norwegian technology in this building. We were almost forced into changing the design from a steel roof to a timber roof. We wanted to

Gardermoen Airport interior

maintain the calmness of the building. You understand the sections – and from inside and you can see a couple of yellow blobs on the drawing – those are buildings within the buildings, and there is one huge roof - a big space. There are two buildings of four storeys, almost five, and they contain airport lounges and offices.

From the gable wall the piers stretch out. It is almost like a tee shirt. This is where you depart, and this is the airside, the land side, and that is your arms and the aircraft. So it is very simple to understand, and it should be as simple as that. We were also very concerned about producing a building which was Norwegian. When you arrive at Oslo airport, you should know you have come to Oslo. You are not in Hong Kong, you are not in Los Angeles. You want to be in a Norwegian building. Our client wanted to see it more like a barn, and we said no. Here we are using modern technology, modern design and traditional, natural materials. Unless we can do it in a modern way, we cannot do it. We wanted to make a building, which I like to call "ekemen" in Norwegian or if you like in Nordic, tranquillity – like a quiet monumentality. That is what we set out to achieve, and that means we are using calm surfaces, natural materials, light, simplicity and clarity of layout and talking about the openness – from above – but also we felt that an airport is a national manifestation in a way. It should also reflect the open democratic society. It might sound a bit silly, but it was actually quite serious at the time. When you arrive at the airport to depart, you come along this elevator road, and you come towards the terminal building as you can see there, and the tower which is pointing up on the left hand side. Once we won the competition, we had the responsibility of designing the terminal building, the piers the tower and the railway station, whilst other architects were designing other parts of the masterplan. We wanted to make it more like an aeroplane – a structure which reflected the movement of travel – as I hope you can see here – both in the way we handled the approach road, and the curve in the middle of the picture. This is actually the roof of the railway station, which is also reminiscent of old shells of a traditional railway station, and then you see the main terminal building next to it. At night it appears like that from the airside, and then you can see this huge glass wall and the piers, coming out at either end. When you come to depart, you are now at the upper level, outside, and you have this wall here which is shorter on this end. It kind of opens up at the other, but the idea of showing you this picture is, there is timber. There is the timber roof, and it has also got tremendous cantilevers – it is cantilevered 15 metres at each end – now the engineers obviously got quite a challenge to sort all these problems. The problem of deflection with the roof, which I will come back to later on. Sitting on the glass wall, the whole structure is very simple. The left-hand side is the departure side, and the other one is the arrival side – sorry it is the departing passenger, and that is the airside. Here you see the tall, tall columns inside the glass wall. They are 1 metre concrete columns supporting the roof. They are 1 metres in diameter. Now why is it that height? I will come back to it a few slides later, but just to mention the principal

A structure reflecting the movement of travel

construction. You are starting off from the ground, and you want to carry the load in the building onto the foundations. There are no load-bearing shafts there. There are no loading walls. These columns carry the whole load and also the whole timber roof. These columns are constructed as post tension vertical members. They are tied to the ground, and designed in a way to carry that load. Here you see we started building the lattice girders, which appear as complete beams, and you can see just to get a feeling of their scale, you can see in this scaffold into the left-hand side we have lower down a person standing there. It is quite a huge structure. Now you can see also the begining of the beam. Now they have got a bottom and a top flange. The undergirth is, in fact, made of a laminated timber, like the hull of a boat, it is shaped like a 'V'. The upper one is square and in between there is a lattice girder. Later on you will see it is being clad with Birch ply to make it appear more like a beam. Looking up at the construction, you can also see how the twin beams are introduced. First we had single beams, but they became so enormous. These beams vary in height from 3 metres to 4.2 metres, so it is tremendous. Now in order to carry that load, we split them in two from the initial one – as you can see you have got beams going all the way along, but then how to transfer the load from the roof, onto the column. We devised steel crowns, and they also have the effect of helping to reduce the span, because they are cantilevering out as you can see. They are picking up a load further out, and thereby reducing the actual load of the span of the timber. Each one of these steel crowns weighs 6 tons, so you are

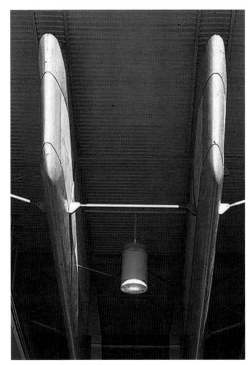

Laminated timber beam

talking about quite big numbers. Here you can see quite clearly how the main beams are being made up and you can see the reinforcement of this column to carry that load. I quite like these kinds of pictures, when buildings are under construction. They are more interesting than when they are finished. Here it is finished, and you can see the tower on the left and here you can also see the covering at the side of the lattice girders with the plywood cladding. At that time, the difference in colour was not just right. We wanted it to be more similar. It seems to be better and merging, after 4 years. It was very important to introduce steel

ties to transfer the load, but it had to be done so you can actually get the load of the whole 4.2 metre depth on the crowns, and onto the columns. It was very important that you got the weight distributed evenly within the depth of the beam.

You can see the lighting is interesting. Here we worked with Lighting Design Partnership of Edinburgh, Andrew Tanners who is an old friend of mine. He was brought in to help sort out the lighting. We wanted natural lighting from an environmental point of view and to use the very minimum of artificial lighting in this airport. We introduced a number of skylights between the twin beams.

The cloth like ceiling – between the beams, is in fact a perforated cloth of metal. We started off with a canvas; it became dirty and difficult to maintain. Here you can see more clearly how the load is transferred from the twin beams onto the crown, with the lighting integrated. Artistic elements and artwork done by Norwegian artists was introduced to the interior. – and it has been quite successful. The lightness of this fabric installation here, I think, has been very successful.

I have left it this long before I give you some facts. The roof measures 136 metres x 183. We say that the roof is reminiscent of the wing on an old aeroplane. The columns are spaced at 18 metres centres. The post tension concrete columns are 1 metres as I mentioned. The beams in pairs have got a 3 metre separation. The cantilevers extend 15 metres and the whole length of the beam is 136 metres. Now this technology – when we started the job – was felt to be absolutely impossible to deal with, so a lot of money was put into research to do it. It is claimed to be the largest timber beam in the world – I don't know if it is still the case, but it was at the time. The longitudinal distance

Gardermoen Airport Terminal Building, Oslo

between the columns is 51 metres. The steel crowns are 1 metre laterally – 3 metre longitudinally, thus reducing the span to 45 metres. Each steel crown weighs about 6 tons. The heights of the beams vary from 2 metre to 4.2 metres. The steel connections have been introduced for lightness in connection between the primary and secondary beams. If you look at it a bit more closely from the airside, you will notice there is a sort of greyish part and a lighter one higher up. This is sun shading. The deflection can be quite substantial – it's deflection due to its own loading, snow loading, wind loading, and also due to changes in temperature. The upper part of the glass wall is attached to the roof and the lower part is attached to the structure. Almost like a shoebox – the main wall is the box where the lid can move up and down. Another issue, which is nothing to do with timber, but I think it is quite interesting – from that size of glass wall you get quite a down draught. Here, you can see some fins. They are in cherry wood, and they are introduced for two reasons:- one is to break up the scale with the distance between the different storeys and the second reason to make a screen so you cannot see up into the spaces, so you have some privacy.

When you arrive by aeroplane, going into the building you are met not by glass walls, but a timber part of the walls. You are actually coming into a timber environment. The piers have actually got a laminated beam structure, the main structure, sitting on smaller crowns, and on concrete columns. And here you can see the beams with some clerestorey lighting introduced at certain intervals, because the whole building –from end to end – is almost 850 metres. Everything you touch should be touched. You walk on the timber floor, it is in oak. You have got the cherry counter. This was at the gate.

Now we move on to just very briefly to the railway station. We designed the railway station. Here, again,

you are being met by a timber roof and a timber sofit. Timber structure, timber sofit and here a timber structure. This is the slide of the station, and this is the end of the terminal. So there is quite a lot of timber introduced on the outside. This is part of the railway station roof. Here you see it under construction; timber beams, but they are actually sitting on a steel structure. The feeling is very much of a timber structure. I mentioned briefly that the materials you touch – and here you have got a timber floor and timber handrail – this is a combination of Maple and Cherry. At every junction we introduced steel, to make it more precise, but it is predominately timber. We devised special brackets to attach the glass. Even when you get your ticket and you go to the counter – you don't have big long timber counters – the timber is sitting on the steel.

Finally, we were very pleased that the government wanted to spend lots of money on art in the building. The artwork of the paper clip, is one of the very few Norwegian inventions.

Artwork of paperclip set into flooring

Timber handrail of Maple and Cherry

HEALTHY DESIGNS AND HEALTHY BUILDINGS

John Gilbert, John Gilbert Architects

Why is it that we Scots seem to run away from nature, yet the Finns and Scandinavians seem to embrace it? At the first opportunity the Scandinavians will be off to their summer lodge house by the lake. It is great to walk down a Swedish street on a Saturday afternoon if you want to do your shopping, because it is totally empty, they are all out in the country communing with nature! I remember visiting Hvittrask in Finland and walking down through a forest and into a lakeside jetty. Everything was quiet and serene, to the right of me was a naked man standing at the verandah of a little cottage, looking out at the lake. Meditating.

I would love to be able to do that in Scotland, but we have a different culture.

I will be showing examples of different architects work, not all my own at all, because I am by no means a specialist in timber.

Pearce Brosnan is now used to advertise FSC. To quote the advertisement: "You don't have to be a special agent to specify timber, you just say FSC". Well, actually, I really would like to be more involved in the specification of timber and to know where it comes from. I think a great frustration amongst architects is not actually knowing where the timber comes from. You have a main contractor who sources his timber from his building supplier, so the contractor doesn't know and often the supplier doesn't know. Unless you actually go and source where the timber is coming from you can never be sure of it's origin.

I think we should be agents to try and encourage the use of Scottish timber. There is lots of it. And there are hundreds of different woods that we don't really use, and we don't know enough about. It is good to be able to use natural timbers, but a lot of low grade timber can be processed into engineered products. For example: 'parallel' and 'interlam' beams used in timber kit construction; fibre boards, which you can get here but are generally imported from either Germany or Sweden. Great because they are good insulants and vapour permeable. Other insulated boards like Heraklith which is kind of strawboard with insulation can be used as a base for render. Oriented Strand Board which is made in Scotland, can be used for flooring as well as sheathing. The great thing about the processing is that all of the timber is used, so it is a very

Examples of timber grown in Scotland

economical material to use.

But unprocessed timber, from Scotland? How do you get hold of that, and how is it used?.

Argyll Green Woodworkers is a small group of enthusiasts who have a centre near the Crinan canal. They are trying to educate people about the selection of Scottish timbers and their construction using local Oaks, larch, fir and spruce, and these are just a number of buildings they have put up themselves. This open framed structure is where they make cruck frames. It is an oak cruck frame structure with a larch shingle roof.

It takes some time to be able to source trees that will make suitable trunks - this drawing shows a number of different 'cuts' that can be taken from an oak tree - actually this is for a Viking longship, it is nothing to do with building buildings, but it is useful to explain the

Oak cruck frame structure with a larch shingle roof

great variety of 'cuts'. If you cut the tree down at the base, you would lose the whole keel of the ship.

This is just a small building by a forestry worker, with help from Argyll Green Woodworkers, who did the cruck frame construction. It is Larch clad- an individual house which was not too expensive by private housing standards, however most of the work I do is in the social housing sector, so any construction has to be very economical, and I cannot afford to use truck frames like this example. Ivor Davies has talked a bit about the heartwood, and the problems of using sapwood, which soon deteriorates as you can see from these logs. We use quite a lot of untreated Larch, as long as it is protected and ventilated behind. Where is it coming from? There is plenty of Larch in Scotland that is available from a number of sawmills.

Kilmartin House visitor centre is a very good example of what can be done using local timbers. In this case Nick Pye did the woodwork. Great use of Oak and Hazel, and a very light and airy conservatory. A great place to go.

Natural Power recently moved from Glasgow to a purpose designed office near Castle Douglas. It was designed by Neil Sutherland, who is quite an exponent of timber construction. The office appears to be in the middle of nowhere, 3 miles up a track.. . .as a result, the company encouraged the conversion of staff cars to

Oak framed house by Argyll Green Woodworkers

LPG so commuting would be more economical. The timber building itself uses a whole mixture of Scottish-sourced, local-sourced timbers. A lot from the surrounding forest but also Douglas Firs and Oaks, depending on the need for weather resistance. Rather nice furniture in the lock ups for the boots and hats. Vertical cladding and a turf roof, solar panels, and it is all driven by a mini hydro power facility. A very pleasant working environment - the feeling of the natural timber was great. It was all around you and also the views of the forest and the views out were magnificent. Kind of hard to work in an environment like that! They are presently about to extend the offices, so it has obviously been a success.

This is Cornelius McClymont's office building in Cathcart for Organisational Development Services. It is all warmcell insulation and Cedar clad.

Timber cladding and timber housing has been used for quite some time in Scotland. It is not new. It was encouraged before the War, with certain subsidies, and immediately after the War. So Swedish timber houses like this are still going strong and there is no reason why they should not continue. However there is still an incredible reservation about building new timber housing. I have great trouble convincing clients that they can do this sort of thing. Everybody from mainstream housing association clients, to even self-builders are very reserved about cladding their building in timber, whereas in Swedish housing (this example is in Malmo), it is used extensively. Inside this Swedish demonstration house all of the finishes and construction are timber, using solid wall timber construction and laminated constructions. There is no plasterboard in these buildings. It is all a very hydroscopic and provides an airy, light space. Under-floor heating used in timber floor constructions is common. The Scandinavians often use screeds on top of the timber, incorporating the under-floor heating pipes. They also use fibreboard build ups with underfloor systems,

In terms of Scottish attempts at innovation, although there is a lot of talk about innovation from government and public bodies, there is really very little back up for it. If you are a small housing association or a small client, you are not going to get a lot of help to do anything very innovative, and the market leaders out there will only do it when they have got a market. However funding alone will never create the climate that creativity and true innovation can flourish in. There has to be a strong basis of trust between clients, users, architects and engineers for innovation to flourish. People need to be able to put forward ideas that will be considered with an open mind.

One example of product and material development is the Tradis system where the roofs, walls and floors are prefabricated. Erection of these insulation filled units requires a crane. It needs to be erected very quickly, so that the roof is giving protection to the floors underneath If the roof is not on, the intermediate floor can get soaked and then the moisture starts buckling the panelling underneath. 'Traditional' timber kit construction, avoids this, because it does not really matter if it gets wet until the roof is on. Web beams are another innovation. In a single storey wall construction they can be used top form the wall studs, floors and roof. For two storey, the studs may need beefed up to take the additional loading. You can get this ridiculous build up of 6 studs sandwiched together, simply causing a cold bridge. This sort of detail has to be designed out, so in most cases we have reverted to solid timber studs in kit construction, rather than web beams.

This is the architect Duncan Roberts, who is a very keen exponent of self-build. This is his own house, which he is self building. It is a Walter Segal method of construction where everything is raised off the floor. None of the timbers are preservative treated. He has a flat roof with local sedums which he is collecting from nearby gutters, so they are all local sedums.

Duncan is using sheeps wool to insulate the house (when I asked him what insulant he was using he said "wool! Is there any other type?" He is completely sold on the idea of wool which I would love to be able to use, but I really cannot afford it in social housing yet.

This is another of Duncan's schemes at Benarty in Fife, which is self build, and is all stick built, rather than kit built, so there is quite a lot of work for self builders in putting it up. The frames are Douglas Fir posts -- set on a little piece of lead DPC on a small plinth, so it is a very small footprint, very light and really very simple construction. It took the self builders two years to build 5 houses. The breathing walls uses fibre board and warm cell insulation, and basically as little treatment to timber as possible.

This single storey timber house is by Fraser Brown Newman, a Glasgow practice who developed these houses with Oregon for Rosehill Housing Association. The spruce clad bungalows are painted brown and blue-grey, with a lightweight metal roof.

Whilst architects are recognising the benefits of using timber in house construction and cladding, insufficient thought is given to managing the internal air quality of our dwellings. The tendency to create vapour sealed rooms with hard finishes and higher internal temperatures can lead to higher levels of relative humidity, particularly in late summer periods when the dust mite population increases. Although we design housing to have temperatures of 21 degrees in living rooms, we often find that people have much higher room temperatures - nearly semi tropical. The internal temperature in our housing has been rising for every decade. So, although we insulate our houses more, people's comfort level of heating seems to be going up and up, and that is creating problems itself in terms of health.

Stirling Howieson of Strathclyde University have been researching the effects of the dust mite population. At 80% humidity levels with higher temperatures in summer, dust mite populations increase dramatically, They like warm moist conditions and allergens are given off by the faecal pellets of dust mites that lie in the beds and the soft fabrics of the house. These allergens can trigger asthma attacks which is a growing problem amongst the population. Internal air quality in our dwellings is an important factor which is not addressed under the Building Regulations.

If we could make our building fabric more hygroscopic, changes in humidity could be absorbed by the building fabric, rather than the soft furnishings. We tend to seal our buildings and use hard surfaces, gypsum plasters, tiles and vinyls, so that there is little moisture being taken up in the fabric. Older buildings, with lime plaster and timber, are more able to adjust to these changes in moisture.

People are also more hygienic, so they are not just washing clothes, but also drying them inside, creating more moisture. We have had to look at trying to provide drying facilities in houses as well as providing well balanced ventilation systems.

Culturally, we are not like the Scandinavians or Finns. We don't go out to the country at the weekends. We tend to stay at home far more than we ever did. The internal finishes, fittings and furnishings within our houses, and the increased air tightness of dwellings, has led to concerns over VOC (Volatile Organic Compounds) being released over a period of time. The higher the temperature is inside a house, the more of these VOCs are given off. VOCs are found in the formaldehyde binders that you get in chipboards, flooring, processed timbers, in glues, paints and preservatives. Once again, better ventilation will help reduce VOC levels and avoidance of VOCs is clearly the healthier option.

I would like to show some examples of housing that we have been working on. Our project in Glenalmond Street for Shettleston Housing Association is all timber kit construction, using 160 deep web studs fully filled

Natural Building Technologies: Fibreboard Insulation, Clay 2 lime renders

with cellulose insulation. Externally the building is clad in larch cladding, local brick and rendered panels. We tried to use local materials as much as possible, and a lot of the external landscaping has used recycled products. The houses are heated through a combined geothermal and solar system. Eight flats are accessed from a glazed close which has an internal planted area. All the houses are ventilated through passive stack ventilation. We have also used some solar ventilation so that the air coming into the house is pre-heated by the space between the sarking and the roof tiles. The Larch cladding was untreated, and is designed to be protected and ventilated. As well as bricks, we have recycled floorboards in the loft spaces.

Since most of our housing stock is old, rehabilitation and repair are essential if we are to maintain this asset. Victorian tenements are often thought to be built entirely of stone, but actually it is fully of timber, bricks and lime mortar, all very hygroscopic materials. Timber joists are built into the stone wall, so it is important to control the moisture level of these timbers. When we come to rehabilitate such a building, the fear is we strip out everything, and then we insulate it and put vapour barriers in and seal it, thus changing the make-up of the wall. I have concerns that this approach may actually exacerbate the problem of those joists that are bedded in the wall by preventing the evaporation of any moisture build up near the joist ends We are looking for solutions which do not change the breathable nature of these older properties.

Old property would also use seasoned timber, probably be a bit over-designed, and very hydroscopic whereas the new buildings will usually make use of kiln-dried and treated timbers and use hard plaster and vapour barriers.

Chemical rot treatment is a big problem, often installed by unskilled operatives and often as a palliative to sorting the source of moisture that caused the problem. The Danes have a policy of using heat treatment to eradicate rot spores, slowly heating the whole building up over a number of weeks, keeping it at a constant temperature, and then dropping the temperature off, so you are not getting cracking or shaking of any timbers that are heated. It does take a longer time, but it reaches all the fabric of the building, unlike rot treatments which just tackle one individual bit of it, and of course it does not put preservatives into the building, so it is really very safe, and as long as you monitor the building, and have changed the nature of the building in terms of its moisture content and humidity, that should work. But it does require monitoring and control, and I think that is what puts people off.

Some more sustainable rehabilitation approaches have been tried in tenement refurbishment, like this project in Dumbarton Road by Murray Design. The walls were insulated with blown cellulose in order to create a breathing wall kind of construction. Neil May of Natural Building Technologies has been a strong supporter of ecological products, such as fibre boards and the use of clay and lime renders. It is an approach we are actively considering for such rehabilitation projects.

Not all housing is obviously, old tenements - a lot of it is post war housing which used a lot more concrete. This can be used to advantage because of its greater thermal capacity. We renovated sixteen flats in Lumphinnans (using geothermal energy once again as the heat source). The fabric was externally insulated and all the open balconies converted into sunspaces. We retained all the internal floorboards and tried to repair them as much as possible, rather than strip them out. Drying cabinets were created just off the sun space, and lined it with natural untreated softwood lining with a flax insulant which is hydroscopic. A passive stack vent takes away any excess moist air and air drawn from the sun space helps to dry the clothes.

The sunspaces were a Danish system, which allows each sun space to be opened up into a balcony. There is also an internal bike store for bikes

Finally, we are now on site with a housing project at Leitch Street in Greenock. Our client was keen that we should create a more sustainable approach to housing. The site was an old railway goods yard which was contaminated. The first thing we had to do was cut all the scrub trees down. We used the chippings for a sort of path for the compound. The development incorporates a sustainable urban drainage system which contains surface water drainage under the road layer, then directs the water to three deep soakaways. Although such approaches are being encouraged by SEPA and government, we found considerable difficulty in getting support from the local authority, because they have to eventually adopt the roads, and were very concerned because such an approach had not been tried before,

Our engineer had to provide calculations to show what would happen in Greenock if it rained for 5 days, 25mm, that is two and a half metres of water in 5 days. Now Greenock is wet, but the annual rainfall is about 700 millilitres, and I know global warming is catching up, and it is going to get wetter, but two and a half metres!

We have used timber criblock retaining walls. A lot of the old foundations were recycled with a crusher plant on site and we have used that in some of the make up, and in solum areas. The site is below a hill that is overshadowing the site. A solar study showed where the overshadowing would be which led to adjustment of the housing layout to allow more light to filter through. We put sun spaces on the upper floors in bedrooms, in order to maximise the sunlight.

The designs are relatively simple, and makes use of timber throughout, as well as cellulose fibre insulation, breathing wall-type construction. There is some timber cladding, but not an extensive amount. Posi joists are used rather than web beams.

The warmcell is now is put under pressure, with OSB on the inside. The roof sarking is a breathing fibreboard material, which actually allows us to not vent the roof space. This makes for a more airtight building, although we have still got passive stack ventilation. All of the wood in the kit comes from Scandinavia, and it does not require really high skills to fabricate, it is a very small kind of factory that is building them but it does offer a lot of employment. I think my frustration is that there is not more skill involved in the housing industry. That we still go to Scandinavia for windows and doors, and there is much less manufacture of joinery products than I would like to see in Scotland.

For those of you interested in energy, the scheme is to be heated using a gas fired combined heat and power scheme, thus providing electricity as well as hot water.

And finally, hedgehog heaven. A house that every hedgehog would like. It has got little draft lobby, a green roof, timber walls, and passive stack vent. I will leave you to consider this basic design and I hope we can build healthier houses in the future.

Hedgehog heaven

THE IMPACTS OF CLIMATE CHANGE: DESIGN AND CONSERVATION

Stephen Garvin, Director, BRE Scotland

What I am going to talk about this morning is about climate change and timber, and particularly, the impacts of climate change on construction.

BRE has been involved in research on climate and its impact on buildings ever since its inception about 83 or 84 years ago. Just after the Second World War, BRE put a presence into Scotland by opening an office on the south side of Glasgow and we moved from there in the 70s to East Kilbride. The primary reason for having an office in East Kilbride was to look at the effects of wetter, colder climates on buildings. Round about that time, things like insulation materials in buildings were less known about, and there were many problems with the comfort in buildings, and with condensation, mould growth, dampness, and rain penetration. We also had problems with the materials - 50 years ago there was still a brick industry in Scotland, but that particular industry has changed quite dramatically over the years, where a number of smaller companies are now transporting materials over longer distances in the UK. At the time we had many smaller Scottish brickmakers, but the quality of the materials we had to make the bricks out of were not particularly great - problems such as frost damage were common. So that was one of the original reasons for locating in Scotland, and the expertise that we have in the East Kilbride office of BRE has really developed from that background; those are our roots, and we still have much of the expertise from looking at the thermal performance of buildings, and the problems within buildings –for example, condensation, leading to mould growth on walls, in turn leading to health problems inside buildings for the building users. Rather ironically, we have a team of people who have worked almost full time over the last 4 years to develop Building Regulations relevant to the thermal performance of buildings, centring on the conservation of heat and power. The rather ironic thing is that work is being done directly for the Government departments down in London, as opposed to Edinburgh, although we have had some input there as well.

So, we have always had an interest in looking at the impacts of climate on buildings. Climate change takes us into a slightly different arena. Traditionally when we have looked at the effects of climate on buildings, we have taken historic data - what the climate has been like over the last 50 years, 100 years, 200, 350 years. For as long as we have been measuring temperatures, rainfalls etc., we have been developing British Standards and Building Regulations around about that historic climate. We now know that we have been pumping out greenhouse gases into the atmosphere at such a rate and for such a time that we are making a change in our climate as a result. And, according to the Intergovernmental Panel on Climate Change, that will continue. The IPCC is made up of literally thousands of experts around the world who come together to look at the science of climate change. Some are responsible for developing models of climate change, and therefore estimating what is actually going to happen to the climate on a global scale. Some of the recent reports from the IPCC have suggested that changes to the climate on a global scale are going to be much worse, or much more extreme, than previously predicted. A lot of the prediction is centred around the emissions of greenhouse gases - carbon dioxide in particular, but also other gasses. It is increasingly common to find at least a small item on the news, television, radio, or newspapers on how climate change is impacting on our environment, particularly on the natural environment – earth, water, polar icecaps. Just last night I got half a snippet about the impacts on the natural environment being detected and being attributed to climate change in the islands in the Indian Ocean. Just coming here this morning on the train, I picked up my copy of the Metro thinking I would find something relevant to talk about at this conference here today, and sure enough, there is a picture of a tornado coming over Corstorphine Hill, and this was on Tuesday. I am not sure how much damage it did, but there surely hasn't been very many tornadoes coming over Corstorphine Hill in my lifetime - the climate is changing. We have made a discernible difference to the climate as a result of our activities.

So what I would like to do today is go through some of the background evidence for climate change, to look at how we are assessing that change, and how we develop scenarios of climate change that we can use in estimating the risk to different sectors. In our case, we are particularly concerned about the risk to the construction sector - to the built environment as opposed to the natural environment.

Climate change is caused by the greenhouse gas effect. The greenhouse effect is actually a natural phenomenon, but through our activities we are actually causing quite a change in the greenhouse gas effect.

This change is driven by the emission of greenhouse gases, particularly carbon dioxide, but there are also much more powerful greenhouse gases than carbon dioxide. Carbon dioxide is a concern simply because of the amount that is actually in the atmosphere, but some of the other greenhouse gases, the CFCs, HFSc etc, are much more powerful and potentially much more damaging to the environment. There are even a number of greenhouse gases that are used in industrial processes which, although they do have some benefits, have clear alternatives which should be used in preference. I am not going to talk about mitigation of climate change, which involves the drive to reduce the greenhouse gas emissions, the changes to the Building Regulations Conservation Heating Power, better insulation of homes, more efficient heating systems, boilers etc. Some of that has been Regulated and some of it has been encouraged through voluntary means as well. We set targets – Kyoto, followed up by major conferences, just like the one in Johannesburg, and those are happening every year now. So there is real commitment around most of the world to actually pursue this issue, to look at climate change and try to reduce its effects. But we probably don't have any option but to adapt for climate change. Molecules in the atmosphere like carbon dioxide are very persistent. If we actually stop polluting the world now with carbon dioxide, it would take at least 100 years to fall to something like 60 – 70% of our current loading of concentration of carbon dioxide in the environment. So it is very persistent, and of course, we are not going to stop because we are not going to stop using cars, heating buildings, or burning things that produce the carbon dioxide. We are on a curve with climate change, and it is going to continue.

So, the greenhouse gas effect: to summarise, the sun's short-wave radiation comes in through the atmosphere, it passes through the greenhouse gases, hits the earth, warms the earth, warms our atmosphere, but it is also radiated back outwards from the earth as well. It can in some cases be short wave radiation, but in some cases it is also a long wave radiation, and it is this long wave radiation which gets absorbed by the greenhouse gases and gets directed back to the earth. So we want a bit of that, because it keeps us warm. If we did not have the greenhouse gases, cooling would be very rapid, and so we would not be able to exist on earth, but the more gases we put into the atmosphere, the greater potential there is for warming. I try not to mention global warming, because it is not quite the right term to use (it goes beyond just warming the temperature of the environment - it affects all aspects of the climate). So, why is this happening? Well, there isn't really much argument that greenhouse gas concentration has increased markedly since 1870, and especially over the last century of carbon dioxide emissions to the

atmosphere. We can take cores from ice sheets in the Arctic and the Antarctic etc. and provide proof of that, and we know it is the result of industrialisation. There are of course natural impacts that also cause greater or lesser amounts of carbon dioxide, but we are definitely on an upper trend. Observation of the global temperature shows this to be the case – of course things do vary, but mean temperatures are actually globally on an upward trend:

- If we look at the UK average temperatures for each month in the 1990s compared with the 1961 to 1990 average, over most of the year it has been getting warmer during the '90s than in the previous 30 years.

- Temperature figures in central England, which have been measured for a long time now, obviously have some variability, but towards the end of the last century, the effect of greenhouse gases in the atmosphere and the resultant warming is more apparent. We are predicting further, more dramatic increases with time.

- If we look at changing sea levels measured at various points around the UK, again up to the year 2000, they show a general upward trend, and certainly compared with about 50 years ago, an increase in the sea level. We know polar ice caps are melting, and there is less ice in glaciers etc, but in fact the actual cause of a rise in sea level is probably much more to do with the expansion of the water that is in the oceans at present, rather than the melting of the ice caps. That is going to have a much longer-term effect on the sea level. But generally we are on an upward curve of sea levels.

- Storm surges. If we increase the sea level, then storm surges are going to become more critical. Critical periods, the return periods for damaging sea storm surges, are going to reduce. Think of the great weather and flood catastrophes over the last 40 years - we are seeing much more loss through natural events, flooding etc. There has been much debate recently about whether insurance companies should continue to insure buildings which are in flood plains, and we know as a result of increased sea level heights, other climate factors, that flooding is likely to become more common. Consequently, there are decisions to be made about where we construct buildings and whether insurance companies will continue to insure buildings in certain locations. Of course the government does not want to underwrite the losses which would occur if buildings were not insured for flood.

- Gales - perhaps not quite as clear-cut, but a trend slightly towards more increased frequency of gales, and of course gales, strong winds etc. are some of the most damaging aspects of climate for buildings.

- Rainfall: an interesting one. We are probably looking at an overall increase in rainfall in the UK. It is going to change throughout the seasons, and a lot depends on the emission scenarios, but certainly within the winter periods there is going to be increases in rainfall throughout the UK. More specifically, perhaps the further south we go the greater the increase of the average rainfall, especially during the winter. But overall, we can expect an increase in the amount of rainfall. And in a windy country like the UK, we know that rainfall does not fall vertically - it often blows horizontally, and that has quite an impact on the way that we build and design buildings.

So that is some of the evidence as to why things are beginning to happen. We have been monitoring the climate for hundreds of years and we are beginning to see some evidence of the impacts of man's activity on the climate. However, to get a real feel for how things are going to be in the future – 20, 50, or 100 years from now - we have to use global climate models. A number of models have been developed by organisations in the UK, particularly at the Tindall Centre at the University of East Anglia, and the Hadley Centre at the Met Office. The models are very sophisticated and in order to verify whether they could be used to look at future climate, data is taken and used to model what the climate was like 200 years ago. Using the emissions data predictions for carbon dioxide and other greenhouse gases, the models are used to try and predict how the temperature and rainfall etc might vary across the UK. A set of climate change scenarios, the most recent being in 2002, have been produced by an organisation called the UK Climate Impacts Programme. These scenarios are about trying to make some sense of climate change so that sectors like construction and building are able to determine what effect it is going to have. Other sectors are doing the same: agriculture, natural environment, and forestry will all be very interested in what is going to happen. It is probably not realistic or practical to estimate anything beyond next 100 years. About 10 years ago, there were 6 climate change scenarios, but that was revised in 1988 and was reduced to 4, and at that time they were called high, medium-high, medium, medium-low, and low. These are based on predictions of the amount of greenhouse gas, particularly carbon dioxide, that has been releases into the atmosphere. They have been refined between 1990 and 2002 to take account of things like sulphur dioxide and other particulates in the atmosphere. What the climate change scenario has tried to do is to look the effect of this man-made climate change, in comparison with natural variation (which of course is going on all the time). There is an expectation under any scenario that we are going to continue to pump out carbon dioxide into the atmosphere at quite an alarming rate. Even at the low emission scenario, which involves much greater use of renewable energy, reducing the amount of energy used in buildings and perhaps even reducing the amount of car journeys we make, carbon dioxide levels in the atmosphere will still be quite high. And of course if we just let things run on as they are at present, or let them get worse, we will be having quite frightening levels of carbon dioxide.

We are fairly confident that we can measure how much greenhouse gas is in the environment, and that we can predict using the models how much of an effect it is going to make - we are reasonably confident about predictions of change in temperature, rainfall, and sea level. However, we are currently less confident about the changes in winds, particularly wind speeds. A probable scenario is that we can expect a more frequent return of higher wind speeds, so what was a 1 in 50 year gust perhaps becomes a 1 in 5 year. However, the overall change in wind speed is difficult to predict from the climate models, and this uncertainty is problematic, especially in the built environment, since wind and gales are obviously one of the most damaging aspects of the climate for buildings. Driving rain, although a secondary issue, is also important. Are we going to get more driving rain in the future? What seasons is it actually going to occur in? And soil moisture: are we going to get more vapour transportation, more drying of the soils? And therefore in certain areas, more risk of subsidence? Climate change is going to impact on all aspects of construction - for example, the durability of materials, and the weather-tightness of buildings. How would we deal with higher temperatures? Effective ventilation, or as householders do we start putting in little air conditioning units? They use up a lot of energy: in fact more energy to cool than to heat a house, so again we are pumping out more greenhouse gas to actually run those coolers. The construction process may be affected. More disruption by winds and rain etc will certainly have an effect on the infrastructure. There is certainly a need for sustainable drainage to combat the predicted higher rainfall and more intense periods of rain. The effects of climate change may vary in severity - some of them may be catastrophic (storms, floods etc.), some causing quite severe damage (e.g. structural movements, subsidence causing foundation failure etc.). In the longer term perhaps, durability and component life may be adversely affected by the increase in mean temperatures and changes in rainfall. Storm damage: if we reduce the return period for the gale force winds, we are going to increase the amount of damage we see like this, so how do we actually deal with that? The amount of flooding is likely to increase. Sea-level rises, more storm surges, intensive precipitation, perhaps combined with more risky building; building on flood plains in greater quantities than we have done before. Increased driving rain potentially. We know that we have a tradition of dealing with driving rain in Scotland - overhanging eaves, and the way in which we build our walls. If it gets warmer, we might get less frost, but if we have wetter masonry then when it is frosty, will it cause more damage?

Different materials will respond differently. The response depends on the use of the material, and indeed its end use. A potential issue for timber is its weather tightness and the durability of the material itself. All materials of a porous nature tend to change form when they get wet and dry out, and timber is no exception, so we may have a look at how we protect the timber. The durability coatings: if we get longer, hotter summers – at least in some locations – we are going to have more loading from solar UV light on the coatings and on the sealants. So we are going to have to use the right sealants in the right place, and perhaps develop more resistant formulations. Paints and varnishes etc. may also require more maintenance. Sealants and mastic could also be stressed by the greater movements in buildings due to increased moisture and temperatures. Are we going to stress these materials more, and cause them to deteriorate faster? We have got; for example, work under way with Historic Scotland looking at the durability of historic windows in comparison with some of its modern counterparts. We are looking at the frequency with which we need to maintain these windows. Is it going to change? Are we looking at more frequent periods by 2020, 2050 as the climate changes?

It is important to highlight that we are addressing a current issue here. We have already affected the climate by our greenhouse gas emissions, and that has a knock-on effect on the natural and built environments. I think the task of the construction industry is to respond to this change for existing structures, and to examine the issues involved with timber. We have already done work using the climate change scenarios which tries to make estimates of what might actually happen to buildings and building materials, but that is very much in a scoping study stage. We have to move on now, and look particularly at the durability of materials and the probable effects of wind and increased flooding on our buildings. I believe we have enough evidence to show that climate affects buildings, and indeed we can estimate how climate change will continue to do this. What we need now is a co-ordinated, planned, and structured programme to look at this, because climate change may perhaps affect buildings in a worse way than we have yet known.

LIFE-CYCLE ANALYSIS

Peter Bonfield, Head of Timber Division, BRE

I prepared this presentation this morning, when I arrived here, and I was very tempted to come up during the discussion session at the end of the last one, and actually to respond to some of the views raised in the previous speaker's presentation, to talk about engineered wood and cladding. There are a very many good things going on. But today I want to talk to you about environmental aspects of timber in construction. Again, having looked at the delegate list, or perhaps we could have our hands up for those that are architects and engineers and that type? Who? Okay. So what I have actually done with my presentation, is I am going to give you a little flavour of what lifecycle assessment is all about, but what I want to do is to tell you people about how you can use it, and what it means to you when you are designing or thinking about building.

We will start with the environment. Environmental issues have been prominent now for 10, 15, 20 years I guess, but we are moving away from the stage now where these were rather ethereal or esoteric things to do, to having much more of a business focus. So there are a number of taxes, and levys and encouragement now to do the right thing environmentally. There is a landfill tax, climate change levy, carbon trading, and packaging regulations: these are all fiscal incentives, imposed by government, to make people make a difference when it comes to environmental choice. Ethical investment and social housing and things like this are providing new incentives for people to make the right choice, environmentally, So ethical investment, for example, a lot of these very investment houses have big stakes in these construction companies, and they are going to these construction companies and saying look, if you want to retain your stake in this company, we want you to do something to improve your environmental performance, and this is forcing housebuilders and others to do things they have never had to do before, in such a way and think about the environmental issues.

Social housing is another issue. I understand you will get more help if you show and can demonstrate that your social housing project is doing things in the right environmental way. But what is very important now, and again the step change has happened in the last few years, is that doing good things in Greenie way is not just about environment, it is also about sustainability. And that is about sustainability in its broadest sense, so that is linking environmental, social and economic aspects together.

So what I want to do now is to relate that with timber and timber products and the timber products in construction, and to deal with the 3 main issues of where we source the timber from, and the impacts and the sustainability issues around timber in construction.

So sourcing and certification: you will have heard from David Bills yesterday, who will have told you about the progress that the Forestry Commission has made towards demonstrating that wood that comes from our forests in the UK is sustainably managed. Those forests are managed in a responsible way that deals with species, and wildlife, and social aspects as well as economic aspects. But actually the are a number of schemes around now. The timber industry has made quite a great deal of progress around the world on developing ways of demonstrating that these products actually quite well. These products are sourced from good forests. Not all the forest are good, there are still problems in different parts of the world but certainly when it comes to European sourced timber, really there is little problem now, and indeed in other pockets around the world, you can be sure that the timber you are purchasing has come from responsibly and well-managed forests, and these are some of the schemes you will probably come across. However, when it comes to what you might do practically – so if you are designing a building or thinking about what materials you might use, and the sorts of questions you might ask – what is very possible, but still is not the norm now for people to think about where their timber is coming from, and we have been working now with some very small and some very large clients from the construction industry and infrastructure companies, to help them develop plans that have an aspirational vision abut where the timber is going to come from in the future. Some of them are not using – they have not done anything about looking at where their timber is coming from, and it is actually quite a step change to go from that position to one where you know where all your timber comes from. So there are plans to sort of increase the percentage that is used. The government are also looking at this issue, and are about to launch a new government procurement policy that addresses these sorts of issues. I have to say the document is rather complicated at this stage: it deals with legal and sustainable procurement and in fact they are going to appoint a sort of centre of expertise within government to advise the local authorities and different government departments on where to procure timber from. Green and eco homes, we shall talk about in a few minutes. Environmental assessment methods, which also give you credits for timber sourcing. But the timber sourcing issue is not the same negative issue it might have been 10 years ago. A great deal of progress has been made and you can have a lot more confidence now that the timber you are using has come from well managed sources.

Okay, looking at environmental issues again. As I mentioned, 20 years ago or so, environmental issues were greenie, you could not really touch them, you could not touch them. You could not quantify them, so a technique called lifecycle assessment was invented, or created or developed, I guess, as a method of quantifying environmental impacts, and I just want to go through that with you now. Some of you may be familiar with this. Basically what we do within a lifecycle assessment is we look at everything that is going into a process, and everything that is going out of a process. Having at the beginning decided what the scope of our study is, is it the production of timber in a sawmill; is it a house from its inception through to final destruction; whatever? So we set that. We then bring in data. We look at all the things that come in, in terms of raw materials and energy, and water, and whatever else there might be, and we look at all the things that come out in terms of products, and waste and pollution and those sorts of things, and then we do a balance around that. We analyse that, and we put that into different categories, and we go through this process of classification, characterisation, evaluation. So when we characterise the information, we actually look at those outputs from the process, and put them into different categories. So for example, if you are using fuel, if you are using energy, there is a global warming potential and you will see there on the far bar graph there is a CO_2 equivalent of global warming. So that is where we are taking all these bits and bobs that go into the process and allocating them to the impact category.

There are various other impact categories across the bottom here, and in fact there are 12 or 13 that are usually used, that deal with mineral extraction and various other aspects. But then what we had to do is, I mean this is just an arbitrary scale for illustration here, but what we have to do then, is take that per-ton data, whatever it might be, and to convert it into a scale, a normalised scale that allows us to assess what that means. Like is 30 global change bad, or good, there? We don't know. Then we normalise it. And the way we have normalised it here is we have looked at the environmental impact that one UK citizen would generate, and we have calibrated it against that. And you can see that the previous graph looks rather different when you actually normalise it, and you see that for this process, that global warming is not such an issue.

You then have to go through the evaluation stage. So you have to think about what is important to you. If you are living in Liverpool, and there is a factory on your doorstep, what might be important to you might be the lorries and trucks and the local pollution that might come from that factory. So the way in which you might interpret that data might be different to what it might be if you were a government, and you were trying to look at ways of trying to reduce global warming, for example, then you have a different perspective. So how you actually judge the data, at the end of the day, varies.

To try and simplify the process, and I am going to show you some very practical tools you can use in your everyday life to cope with the environmental issues, but we have also developed a system called the eco point system which is where we take the various environmental impacts which are illustrated on the far side of this slide. We have quantified them. And then we do a balancing, and come out with a single point number, and again we have gone through a rigorous process of developing those, so what we can do is we can take all these different environmental impact categories and take them down to a single robust quantified number.

Now our forest industries, our UK forest industries in particular, but also materials coming from overseas and Europe – and we are just looking at our timber frame industry now – have actually done a lot to actually quantify the environmental impacts and their processes. There is this general feeling that using wood is a good thing, you know its renewable, natural all those sorts of things, but what we want to be able to do here is to able to quantify those impacts and be able to objectively judges them against other products and things. So the industry has been very active in actually measuring and proving its case and in fact we have just issued this BRE Digest that quantifies these things. I have a few here with me, and if any of you want these, I would be happy to give them to you. Otherwise you can get them from that email address. Anyway we have had a larger project at BRE run by my colleagues in the Centre for Sustainable Construction. We have actually looked at pretty well all construction materials and we have looked at the environmental impacts around producing those materials and their use in buildings, and that has given us an enormous database of information, and what we have tried to do is to then put that into formats that people can practically use.

So the Environmental Profiles Database is the basic building block if you like, and if any of you are research minded or want to go into detail and interrogate where all these environmental impacts have come from, that is the place to get it. There is a publication about it.

If you want to make your life a little bit simpler we have something called the Green Guide for Specification, and this is – you can see the book there - basically what we have here is we have a construction element, in this case it is an upper floor, but it might be a wall or a ceiling or a roof or a window or whatever. We have a range of constructions, typical construction so in this case it is hollow precast reinforced slab and screed, but it might be the other alternatives, they are the common alternatives. Across the top here we have the different impacts like climate change, fossil fuel depletion, and then we have a simple ABC rating, and that is based on the output of our environmental profiles database. C is bad and A is good. For each of these issues, you can look at what ratings a different solution has, and at the end you get a summary rating that gives you an overall … it is a very simple way, tabular format, of looking up and seeing what, how different alternatives might affect the environmental performance of the building. The great thing is, if you are a timber person, in every construction element – walls, whatever – the timber comes out very favourably. That is the timber solution.

When we are looking at environmental impacts, we don't compare materials. We have to think about how those materials are used, that is what counts at the end of the day, and usually the timber solution comes out as being a very good solution. You know with things like climate change, it has very positive aspects. This is this Digest that we have just produced. As I say, we have some of these here, but we have another tool as well, which may be of interest to you. This is something called Nvest, so if you look at the top corner of the figure here, you see there we have got a layout of a building – and you have all sorts of layouts you can design in there – and into that you can put in all the different sorts of construction you want, whether you are using timber floors or whatever. What this system does for you, again based on our Environmental Profiles Database, and our knowledge of how buildings perform, it will then categorise and measure the environmental impacts on different parts of your building. So here you can see how the floors, walls, windows, roofs etc make the contribution to the overall eco points rating which is given there. Now this is helpful. You have got all these complex things on structure, on the different environmental impact categories, but because we have this eco points system, it actually boils down to a simple number. And what you can do is you can tweak that environmental cost against real cost, and come up with an optimum solution.

You can also look at things like the balance between the operating environmental impacts of the building and the environmental impacts that come actually from making the building. And, again, your needs there might be different. If you are looking at long term maintenance, for example, that is an issue and we find often that cost issues are linked very closely with environmental issues, so if you reduced for example operational and environmental impacts, you are probably reducing environmental operating costs as well. Then we have some system along the bottom here you can see BREEAM, Eco Homes, these are all credit-based systems which encourage small sustainable use of products and better environmental use of products. So in BREEAM for example we have a scoring system – I think it is something like 30% of all commercial buildings now are BREAM assessed and it looks at how the building is designed, at its management, at is control systems, at the materials you use, and you have a credit system. So for example if you get your timber from the right places and that sort of thing, you will get credits. If you have got very good energy efficient design, you will get credits. And Eco Homes is actually the system which is encouraging social housing. So if you get an Eco Homes good, or very good, rating then you can get more money from the housing corporation towards your project. And in fact we have just got an initiative we are working on with WWF in the offices of the Deputy Prime Minister, again to try and encourage better sustainable design in the use of homes. So there are some of the tools we have.

I want to finish now by looking at sustainability and thinking what it means for the timber sector. Again, just to start from the beginning, sustainability is about environmental, social, and economic aspects, okay, it is those things pulled together, or whatever, and I think in the past there has always been a perception that if you are doing things right by the environment, then it is probably going to cost you more. Well we are finding that is not the case. Now the timber industry has been very proactive in developing its own statement of where it is with respect to sustainable development in the UK, and it has also given a statement on where it wants to be in the future, and this is because the Prime Minister, in preparing for the World Sustainability Summit, which was recently held in Johannesburg, he challenged 5 key industries to give them their current position and their aspirations for the future, with regard to sustainability, and the sectors he identified were Finance, Tourism, Water, Energy and Timber & Wood products. So the timber industries, the forest industries and all the downstream users, the imported people, the paper industry, they all got together and produced their statement and their vision for the future. And it is very good actually. It is very much action-focused, and target-focused. It is not just a lot of glossy and written eloquent words. It is actually saying this is what we are going to do, this is what we are going to achieve, and this is what we are going to measure to prove we have got somewhere, and it is really rather positive.

Just to give you some ideas of what has come from that, these are some of the key issues. So on the environment, sourcing timber, environmental impacts, waste, transport energy and biodiversity have come from it. But just again to give you some more specific examples of how these things work together. When you start talking for example, to the sawmilling sector about sustainability, and if you start talking about economic sustainability, how are you going to be in business in this very, very challenging commodity market, in a year and in 3 years and in 5 years? They are looking at products that have added value. Can they save on the unit cost of production. Can they be more efficient? And that efficiency often involves things like reducing energy, reducing fuel, reducing raw material, reducing waste, reducing packaging, and then if you link that with environmental impacts at the top, if you do any of those things, they are going to improve your environmental impact. So the two go very well together.

If we look at social aspects, health and safety or training and education, if you have got a company there where you are really reliant on your workforce to do a good job for you, if you look after their welfare, and ensure they are well trained, then they will do a better job for you. So these things can be harmonious and can

work together, and this is very much the spirit in which this thing has been developed, and that is why I am quite so confident that the strategies can actually deliver some positive change.

Conclusions: really progress on sourcing and certification in sustainable forest management things. There really has been progress there, and you can do the right thing there now. The Environmental Profiles for timber products in various solutions is very good. Sustainability is being seriously considered by the industry, and you will see changes and improvements, even though it is already doing very well.

I would love to talk to you about technical developments. Some of the things they are doing with innovation and engineered products and preservatives and coatings, is fantastic, there are real positive things happening. I would love to show you my pictures. You architect people like good pictures of things, don't you. I have got some fantastic pictures to show you, and that is really encouraging for people like us who are trying to push innovation within a sector. And I will finish with "Wood is Good". You shouldn't feel bad about using trees, it is good. Provide people with the commercial incentives to plant more trees and we will all benefit.

MODERN TIMBER FRAME

Stewart Dalgarno, Stewart Milne Timber Systems

I am very proud to be associated with this conference, actually, because I think it does link in the heritage of Scotland and how we have used timber to maximise it to our benefit and the fondness the whole of Scotland has for using it in the built environment. My presentation today takes me into timber frames in the modern day context and really begins to look at volume, in terms of house building, and what we need to be doing across the wider remit of the UK. So it takes in a manufacturer's perspective of modern timber frame. We are going to look at the market place and how it has evolved over the last period, and where it will evolve to in the future, to look at how product development has evolved - what we have used in the past, and what we may use in the future. How we are going to make these things, utilising the latest skills of IT and robotics and automation. That really is the way forward for our industry. Look at the whole build process and how we can maximise the benefits of timber in the built environment, to ensure that we actually get something that is commercially attractive, which is always at the back of our thoughts. Design: house design is changing and how do we need to transfer information down the line to clients and machine, rather than by endless reams of paper. And how the materials, supply chain and raw materials are required to pull together a house. And most of all, how does it affect the customer, particularly in the industry because at the end of the day the house is somebody's home, and we have got to make sure that the consumer who buys that home, is proud of it.

The Market

We all know the market for timber frame – as Ivor has already alluded to – in Scotland is favourable for us. It is a mature and stable market place. 20,000 houses being built in Scotland every year, of which 60% is timber frame. A proven product and a proven market place. However, it is a different picture, totally, in England and Wales. A real growth opportunity: 170,000 houses being built every year south of the Border, and less than 10% using timber frame. A huge opportunity to use the Scottish knowledge, and penetrate into the built environment south of the Border.

What is the product? The open panel systems, stud work, sheathing and loose joists have served us well

Manufacturing the modern timber frame

over the past 10 – 15 years. The whole culture of the building site now accepts its use in Scotland. We need to use this to establish ourselves in the English market place. We have seen how the product has developed into more cassette floor systems for safer working areas, utilising crane for lifting to prevent manual handling, larger wall sections. Ideal for brownfield development which the Government is pushing because of restrictions in available land in the Green Belt. In the future, perhaps, this is what we will be building, something that is maybe more totally finished in the factory. This product here is a Swedish product, which is fully finished on the outside with timber cladding and finished inside with plasterboard as well. Fully insulated with the windows and doors fitted, 200mm thick, thermally efficient. The whole side of a house is ready for delivery to that particular customer.

Moving forward, maybe this is where we will move to, but to make that product in any degree of volume to satisfy the house building market requires technology. The customer is looking for more nowadays. They are far more educated and demanding. They are far more travelled. They know what they want, and they put harder demands on us all. Skills: we have already heard about the skills shortage, and I am particularly encouraged to see so many students here to learn about timber, and utilise it in the future. Health and safety, environmental credentials to name a few inefficiencies, is moving in favour of timber at the moment. We need to capitalise in the house building market place to provide quality. We have seen how we started off with stick build and cruck frames and some glorious examples of real craftsmanship, but we have quickly moved on to semi-automated factories to produce our timber frame in any real volume. We are currently utilising the manufacturing technology in cross cutting, where we are batch cutting maybe 5 or 6 houses from one operation, and one standard length, minimising waste. Most of the current factories in our industry are manually operated which have got very productive outputs, but in less than work-like fashion. We need to give our own people in the industry a working environment they want to work in, where they are not totally manually orientated, where they are lifting things that they shouldn't be, where they are nailing things in dangerous areas. So we do need to move on, as an industry, and embrace new technology. Begin to look at other industries that have maybe already done so. The car industry has already brought up this assembly line approach and this is really where major investment is required as an industry, where Stewart Milne has taken it to the next level, spending £10 million to build a new factory that utilises this technology. The process is from the raw materials to the automated assembly lines, through to automated nailing stations, lifting devices to allow insulation to be applied and through the conveyor belt system. The plasterboard is fixed to the frame, which is then laid vertically for the final fix of windows and doors. The whole is then transferred by carousel and the completed wall system is ready for the delivery.

This technology is real: this is a photo of our new plant down at Witney – you can see the airbed saw on the right hand side here. Takes a piece of OSB 4.8 metres long by 2.4 metres wide, and in one operation will cut a window and door element out and with a pick and place machine, put it on to the partition. Again, looking at PLC technology on the line here, the production line process, whereby the operator is pulling down information from the design office, in exactly what elements he needs to manufacture. Colour coded touch screen technology so that once that workstation is complete, we can track the progress of any house being manufactured at any one point in time, very similar to what is happening in the car industry. Nailing: we want to ensure that every nail is fixed in the right place, and be sure that every one is at the right penetration depth etc, in a safe working environment, and these nailing bridges really are the way forward to ensure we get guaranteed quality for our frames. Logistics, in terms of just-in-time deliveries, from all our raw material suppliers, including the timber world – be it Scandinavian or home-grown – and a just-in-time principle so that we can maximise output and feed it into our manufacturing lines and develop a quality product. Similarly, we then need to feed that onto site, and we need to be very efficient at how we haul these things along the countryside. These are going to be high-value components in the future, elements that will require a fair degree of protection in handling pieces of furniture; not elements that can be laid down in the mud. It needs to be co-ordinated with the build process on site.

The build process: brownfield site development. We have all heard about it. It is coming at us. The Government is encouraging us to use and develop systems to utilise the land within our own cities, before we use and gobble up the Green Belt. Timber frame offers a solution that benefits the developer, utilising crane in difficult inner city developments. Now the Building Regulations are changing, and harmonising between England/Wales and Scotland. We can reach 6 and 7-storey structures. This is where we really need new innovation in our products. In its commercial applications, key players such as Whitbread have realised the benefits of timber frame. An example of this is a 40 bed travel inn. Back in 1994, Whitbreads looked at how they could increase the brand image of Travel Inn, and how they could penetrate a potential niche in the market for low budget hotel accommodation. They looked at volumetric, steel framed, timber frame and masonry. They came up with timber frame as the way forward for them, almost 10 years ago. Back in '94 they were taking 26 weeks to build a typical 40-bed travel inn. Now with the systems that have evolved, and the developed products, we are doing it in 12 weeks. That is a considerable saving and overall cost reduction but, most importantly to Whitbreads, from the commercial sense, a fairly major increase in revenue. Our little part of providing a structural frame takes 9 days now. I don't think I need to go too much into the environmental benefits. I think we all know here that waste is going to become far more onerous in the future. Accordingly, we are doing more in the factory to minimise waste by using technology.

Embodied energy: I do think we need a rating for our homes nowadays. How much has this really cost the whole process in terms of embodied energy?

Somebody talked about engineered structures earlier on. They are becoming far more engineered. Progressive collapse, disproportionate design criteria, up to 6 and 7 storeys now needs to be evolved through modern timber frame technology. We are seeing component manufacturers – we talked about I-beams and metal web beams and stressed skin panels. These

elements are all required by our industry to ensure that we have got the components as well, to bring about the innovation as a system solution.

Design: a key thing. How many times have we said to each other, I hope we'd spend more time at the front end, because if you don't, at the back end you have got no chance to get it right. So we need to be upfront and work with our architects and engineers and design partners. We have seen how design can now be fed through in downtime transmissions into production. But this is only the start of it. Nowadays, technology to drive these machines, and particular the machines at Witney requires HMI – human machine interface – it all sounds very futuristic, but it is about robotics and automation. These are the areas that will drive the machines and the tools of the future for any real volume. We need to transfer data in an IT world through Computer Data Transfer files. CDT – a whole new learning curve for our industry. How design can interface with manufacturing in a true CAD/CAM environment. Again, this is prevalent in the car industry, to use the same analogies. We can learn from how they have done that successfully, and develop our industry. We have already seen a lot of IT already kick in. We used to have 30 drawing boards in Stewart Milne. We have got none now. It is all work stations and we communicate by email. We have got projects in the Falkland Islands. We have got designers in Australia that work for us now. We have seen this integration already, and we need to continue to develop.

Now, the supply chain. Well this is what it is really about. It's about using home-grown or Scandinavian, but there's a huge market for home-grown here. It is about how can we use our knowledge in Scotland to penetrate the real market place south of the Border. We need to have efficient supply chains with managed

forests for harvesting, conditioning and processing in the sawmills to produce quality, stress-grade, kiln-dried, regularised, packaged and delivered. This example is from Scandinavia, where we get the majority of our timber. I am glad to say we have now a fairly major project with Forest Holidays, which is part of the Forestry Commission. This will be the first time that Stewart Milne will have used any great amount of home-grown timber, and it allows us to experience its unique qualities.

Treatment: somebody talked about treatment earlier on. Ideally, we would like to take that out of the process. Good detailing, good material specification would allow that. If we cannot, we need to have a supply chain in place that allows us to treat timber before it then comes in truckloads, and co-ordinated deliveries into our factories, for processing.

Our customers have significantly changed over the last 5 years. We used to have 250 customers. Our business is focused on the volume market place. Accordingly, we have focused on the top 20 housebuilders; we are now dealing in the private, social and commercial sectors with key partners. We have seen our partnership evolve far more into the front end. This little graph actually shows the whole lifecycle of a project, from its inception right through to its completion. At the tender stage here, we get a batch of drawings, and price a job. Then, obviously we can input in to this and then complete. But through working in real partnership and teamworking with our customers, and evolving new buildable solutions that are going to be attractive for the consumer, we need to be involved at the front end, where we can put an awful lot more value into the project, free of charge. Just to ensure that at the end of the day there is a repeat order on the back of it.

We need to be innovative. We need to think about how strong our industry association is. We know timber is a major threat to the traditional housing bureau in England where brick and block is commonplace. They see that as a major threat to their market place. We need to have a strong industry voice, industry trade association that really penetrates into government, where major decisions are being made on how houses will be built in the future, and to back this up we need to use people like UKTFA, BRE and TRADA to encourage and develop new Ideas. I am glad Phil Bonfield today can give so much background as to where we want to use materials in the future as we see the changes emerging.

We have not talked too much about training. We have talked a lot about craftsmanship, but what are we doing to actually replace them? In the last 10 – 15 years, the construction industry has not been very efficient at taking people in and actually training them up. It is a sorry state, so we need to look at new ways of solving things. We need to educate people. We need to educate a lot of people south of the Border on the benefits of timber frame and how we should be doing it correctly, particularly in housebuilding.

So is it a revolution, and is it innovative? Yes, I believe it is, through the use of our design, through maximising IT, through our materials, through looking at new forms of engineered wood products, and new material supply chains, through our manufacturing technology. Gone are the days of nail guns and a couple of benches. The future might be something different: a fully automated plant.

Our build process: we need to tie in with the contractors and the housebuilding firms, to ensure they know how to understand and how to maximise the product. Is it sustainable? We all know that. Of course it is. Yes. Raw materials: wood is good. We should be proud of using it. Proud development: there are plenty of areas we can develop, and there is plenty of back up and expertise that we could maximise. Processes and how we should be doing things better: yes. People. We need to keep people. Our designers need to know about IT skills and we should encourage new design, including coming from universities and colleges and schools into our environment.

So to finish off, Stewart Milne Timber Systems: we are investing in the future, in a volume timber frame market place. I believe there is a huge opportunity for the timber industry south of the Border, to really capture a big chunk of that housebuilding demand down there. We have got that experience in Scotland. We all know it and love it, and we have been able to discuss it for 2 days here today. To finish off, I have got a clip of the factory at Whitney, just to give you an idea of some of the technology. It is a £10 million investment for ourselves and hopefully, we will be able to show some of the real technology coming through. I would encourage our own industry and other fabricators to come to the fore, because if timber frame does kick off, then we have got to maximise and ensure the capacity is there to service the demand our industry needs to understand the technology that is in timber frame nowadays, and the investment that is required. Major players in our industry are really having to commit to this level of investment. We think it is the right way forward. We need the supply chain in place. I think there is an opportunity to maximise home grown for the benefit of sustainability, and I would like to encourage everyone to promote timber frame. Hopefully, in the future, we can all be proud of it and look at buildings that Historic Scotland can look at 200 or 300 years on and say, we were proud to be part of that development.

MAGGIE'S CENTRE

Design by Frank O Gehry & Gehry Partnership

James Stephen, James F Stephen Architects (Executive Architects)

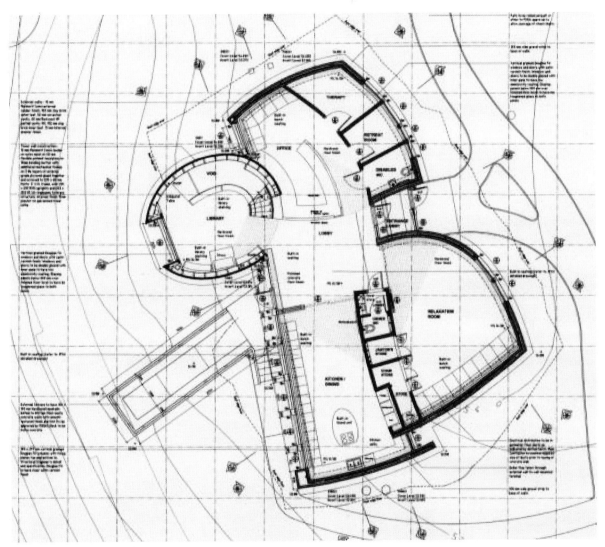

Working drawings - Ground floor layout

Design and landscaping development model. View from the south

Measuring up and part assembly in the workshop

Interior shot of roof

View from north showing roof building